No-N
Extra Class
License Study Guide

(for tests given between July 2020 and June 2024)

Dan Romanchik KB6NU

ISBN: 978-0-9832216-5-4

DEDICATION

Dedicated to my lovely wife, Silvia, who has been extremely patient and accommodating over the years.

ACKNOWLEDGMENTS

Thanks to everyone who proofread and commented on the sections I've posted on my blog, especially Frank, WA8WHP. Thanks, also to Jeff, K1NSS, of Dashtoons fame, for the cover design. Jeff's covers have taken my books to the next level.

And, last but not least, thanks to all my readers. It's very rewarding for me to be able to help you all have more fun with amateur radio.

CONTENTS

WHY YOU SHOULD GET YOUR EXTRA CLASS LICENSE

The Amateur Extra Class license is the highest class of license in the United States, and perhaps the world. Many hams—even hams that live outside the U.S.—aspire to pass the test and be awarded one.

There wasn't always an Amateur Extra Class license. The Extra Class license, as we know it today, was created as part of the 1951 license restructuring, that also created the Novice and Technician Class licenses. (In 1951, the Novice license was the "beginner's license." To get a Technician Class license, you had to pass the written exam for the General Class license.)

Although it gave an operator no additional privileges, to get an Extra Class license, one had to:

- Pass a 20 wpm code test (Generals had to pass only a 13 wpm code test).
- Pass a longer and more difficult written examination than the General Class exam.
- Have at least two years of experience as a licensed radio amateur.

Today, without the code test and the experience requirement, many hams upgrade to Extra Class as soon as they can. Some even pass the Technician Class, General Class, and the Amateur Extra Class exams in a single test session.

So, what's the attraction? Why should you upgrade to Extra?

One of the reasons that you should upgrade to Extra is that you get to use the entire 80 m, 40 m, 20 m, and 15 m bands. Portions of those bands, such as 3.6 – 3.7 MHz in the 75m band and 14.150 – 14.175 MHz in the 20m phone band, are reserved exclusively for Extra Class licensees. Extra Class operators also have exclusive privileges in the CW portions of the 80 m, 40 m, 20 m, and 15 m bands. These are the frequencies where the DX stations hang out.

Another reason to get your Extra Class license is that only Extra Class licensees can administer General Class and Extra Class license exams. General Class operators can become Volunteer Examiners (VEs), but they are only allowed to administer Technician Class exams.

Another reason you might want to get an Extra Class license is to get a fancy vanity callsign. Only Extra Class operators can apply for 1x2 or 2x1 callsigns, such as W8RP or KW1L. A short, snappy callsign can help you work more DX and improve your contest scores.

Whatever your reason, studying for the Extra Class exam will open your eyes to many aspects of the hobby that you may not be familiar with. And, as you work your way through the material, you will learn things that make you a better radio amateur and enable you to enjoy the hobby more. Based on the comments I've had from many readers, I'm convinced that this study guide will not only help you get your Extra ticket, but in the end, help you have more fun with amateur radio.

My own story

I didn't take the Extra Class test until 2006, 35 years after I got my Novice license and almost 30 years after I got my Advanced license. At first, it was the 20 wpm code test that put me off. At that point, I wasn't getting on the air enough to get my speed up to 20 wpm. Later in life, I was afraid that I'd actually fail the written test. Besides, I had a good comeback whenever I was asked why I didn't have an Extra Class license. I used to joke that I wanted to be the last living Advanced Class licensee in the U.S.

After I started teaching amateur radio classes and publishing these license study guides, I decided it was time to get the Extra. Besides, some of my students had already gotten their Extra Class licenses, and I found it a bit embarrassing to have "only" an Advanced Class ticket. So, in 2006, I decided it was time to study and take the test.

I used the ARRL study guide. It did the job, and the test was actually a little easier than I'd anticipated. Even so, I answered three questions incorrectly. I don't know that I'd have done any better if there had been a "No-Nonsense" study guide available for me to use, but my guess is that it would not have. There are just so many things that you have to memorize that you're bound to forget something.

At first, I wasn't planning to produce an Extra Class study guide. I am basically a lazy person, and I knew that writing this study guide would take a long time. The Extra Class question pool covers a lot more material than the Technician Class and General Class exams, and the material is a lot more complex, too.

In the end, though, I knew that I had to do it. Every week, I'd get e-mails from readers asking if or when a *No-Nonsense Extra Class License Study Guide* was going to be available, and my product lineup was incomplete without it.

That was eight years ago, and this is the third edition of the *No Nonsense Extra Class License Study Guide*. I sold thousands of copies, and it makes me feel good that I have been able to help so many become Extras and enjoy all that amateur radio has to offer.

How to use this study guide

First, keep in mind that this is not a textbook. It's not meant to teach circuit theory or antenna theory. Instead, it's meant to put the questions on the Extra Class test in context and help you pass the test. What some readers do is to follow along with the ARRL Handbook or Google topics as they are working their way through the study guide. These sources are able to cover these topics in more depth than I can here.

Question designators, such as "(E5A07)" appear at the end of each question. This is so you can refer to the questions in the question pool, if you would like to. The correct answer, and only the correct answer, appears **in bold** after the question.

Periodically, you should take practice tests. Taking practice tests will allow you to take a break from studying and give you an indication of how well you're doing. You can take practice tests online at ARRL.Org, QRZ.Com, AA9PW.Com, and several other websites.

Good luck and have fun!

I hope that you find this study guide useful and that you'll upgrade to Extra. If you have any comments, questions, compliments or complaints, I want to hear from you. E-mail me at cwgeek@kb6nu.com. My goal is to continually refine this study guide and to continually make it better.

73!

Dan Romanchik KB6NU
cwgeek@kb6nu.com, Twitter: @kb6nu

DAN ROMANCHIK, KB6NU

E5: ELECTRICAL PRINCIPLES

E5A - Resonance and Q: characteristics of resonant circuits; series and parallel resonance; Q; half-power bandwidth; phase relationships in reactive circuits

Resonance is one of the coolest things in electronics. Resonant circuits are what makes radio, as we know it, possible.

What is resonance? Well, a circuit is said to be resonant when the inductive reactance and capacitive reactance are equal to one another. That is to say, when

$$2\pi fL = 1/(2\pi fC)$$

where L is the inductance in henries and C is the capacitance in farads.

For a given L and a given C, this happens at only one frequency:

$$f = 1/(2\pi\sqrt{(LC)})$$

This frequency is called the resonant frequency.

> QUESTION: What is resonance in an LC or RLC circuit? (E5A02)
>
> ANSWER: **The frequency at which the capacitive reactance equals the inductive reactance**

Let's calculate a few resonant frequencies, using questions from the Extra question pool as examples:

> QUESTION: What is the resonant frequency of an RLC circuit if R is 22 ohms, L is 50 microhenries and C is 40 pico-

farads? (E5A14)

ANSWER: **3.56 MHz**

$f = 1/(2\pi\sqrt{(LC)}) = 1/(6.28 \times \sqrt{(50\times10^{-6} \times 40\times10^{-12})}) = 1/(2.8 \times 10^{-7}) = 3.56$ MHz

Notice that it really doesn't matter what the value of the resistance is. The resonant frequency would be the same if R had been 220 ohms or 2.2 Mohms.

QUESTION: What is the resonant frequency of an RLC circuit if R is 33 ohms, L is 50 microhenries and C is 10 picofarads? (E5A16)

ANSWER: **7.12 MHz**

$f = 1/(2\pi\sqrt{(LC)}) = 1/(6.28\times\sqrt{(50\times10^{-6} \times 10\times10^{-12})}) = 1/(1.4\times10^{-7}) = 7.12$ MHz

When an inductor and a capacitor are connected in series, the impedance of the series circuit at the resonant frequency is zero because the reactances are equal and opposite at that frequency. If there is a resistor in the circuit, that resistor alone contributes to the impedance. Therefore, the magnitude of the impedance of a series RLC circuit at resonance is approximately equal to circuit resistance.

QUESTION: What is the magnitude of the impedance of a series RLC circuit at resonance? (E5A03)

ANSWER: **Approximately equal to circuit resistance**

When an inductor and capacitor are connected in parallel, the reactances are again equal and opposite to one another at the resonant frequency, but because they are in parallel, the circuit is effectively an open circuit. Consequently, the magnitude of the impedance of a circuit with a resistor, an inductor and a capacitor all in parallel, at resonance, is approximately equal to circuit resistance.

QUESTION: What is the magnitude of the impedance of a parallel RLC circuit at resonance? (E5A04)

ANSWER: **Approximately equal to circuit resistance**

Because a parallel LC circuit is effectively an open circuit at resonance, the magnitude of the current at the input of a parallel RLC circuit at resonance is very low.

QUESTION: What is the magnitude of the current at the input of a parallel RLC circuit at resonance? (E5A07)

ANSWER: **Minimum**

Conversely, the magnitude of the circulating current within the components of a parallel LC circuit at resonance is high because the circuit within the loop is effectively a series resonant circuit.

QUESTION: What is the magnitude of the circulating current within the components of a parallel LC circuit at resonance? (E5A06)

ANSWER: **It is at a maximum**

High currents circulating in a resonant circuit can cause the voltage across reactances in series to be larger than the voltage applied to them.

QUESTION: What can cause the voltage across reactances in a series RLC circuit to be higher than the voltage applied to the entire circuit? (E5A01)

ANSWER: **Resonance**

Another consequence of the inductive and capacitive reactances canceling each other is that there is no phase shift at the resonant frequency.

QUESTION: What is the phase relationship between the current through and the voltage across a series resonant circuit at resonance? (E5A08)

ANSWER: **The voltage and current are in phase**

Ideally, a series LC circuit would have zero impedance at the resonant frequency, while a parallel LC circuit would have an infinite impedance at the resonant frequency. In the real world, of course, resonant circuits don't act this way. Both inductors and capacitors have a series resistance that needs to be taken into account. To describe how closely a circuit behaves like an ideal resonant circuit, we use the quality factor, or Q. Because the inductive reactance equals the capacitive reactance at the resonant frequency, the Q of an RLC parallel circuit is the resistance divided by either inductive or capacitive reactance, or $Q = X_L/R$ or X_C/R

QUESTION: How is the Q of an RLC parallel resonant circuit calculated? (E5A09)

ANSWER: **Resistance divided by the reactance of either the inductance or capacitance**

The Q of an RLC series resonant circuit is the inductive reactance or the capacitive reactance divided by the resistance, or $Q = X_L/R$ or X_C/R.

QUESTION: How is the Q of an RLC series resonant circuit calculated? (E5A10)

ANSWER: **Reactance of either the inductance or capacitance divided by the resistance**

Basically, the higher the Q, the more a resonant circuit behaves like an ideal resonant circuit, and the higher the Q, the lower the resistive losses in a circuit.

QUESTION: Which of the following increases Q for inductors and capacitors? (E5A15)

ANSWER: **Lower losses**

But, increasing Q has its drawbacks, too. Increasing Q in a resonant circuit will increase internal voltages and circulating currents, and the resonant circuit will have to be made with components that can withstand these higher voltages and currents.

QUESTION: What is an effect of increasing Q in a series resonant circuit? (E5A13)

ANSWER: **Internal voltages increase**

A parameter of a resonant circuit that is related to Q is the half-power bandwidth. The half-power bandwidth is the bandwidth over which a series resonant circuit will pass half the power of the input signal and over which a parallel resonant circuit will reject half the power of an input signal.

We can use the Q of a circuit to calculate the half-power bandwidth:

$$BW = f/Q$$

Let's look at a couple examples:

QUESTION: What is the half-power bandwidth of a resonant circuit that has a resonant frequency of 7.1 MHz and a Q of 150? (E5A11)

ANSWER: **47.3 kHz**

$BW = f/Q = (7.1 \times 10^6)/150 = 47.3 \times 10^3 = 47.3$ kHz

QUESTION: What is the half-power bandwidth of a resonant circuit that has a resonant frequency of 3.7 MHz and a Q of 118? (E5A12)

ANSWER: **31.4 kHz**

$BW = f/Q = (3.7 \times 10^6)/118 = 31.4 \times 10^3 = 31.4$ kHz

Resonant circuits are often used as impedance-matching circuits. Because $BW = f/Q$, increasing the Q of a resonant circuit used for this application has the effect of decreasing the range of frequencies, or bandwidth, over which it can match the impedance between two circuits or between a transmitter and an antenna.

QUESTION: What is the result of increasing the Q of an impedance-matching circuit? (E5A05)

ANSWER: **Matching bandwidth is decreased**

E5B - Time constants and phase relationships: RL and RC time constants; phase angle in reactive circuits and components; admittance and susceptance

Consider a simple circuit made up of a resistor (R) and capacitor (C) in series. When you apply a voltage to this circuit, the capacitor will begin to charge. The rate at which the capacitor charges is dependent on the values of R and C. Similarly, if the capacitor is already charged, it will begin to discharge when you apply a short to the circuit. The rate at which the capacitor discharges also depends on the values R and C.

We say that the "time constant" for this circuit is equal to the resistance in the circuit times the capacitance, or simply R × C. A capacitor charges to 63.2% of the applied voltage or discharges to 36.8% of the starting voltage after one time constant. After two time constants, a capacitor charges to 86.5% of the applied voltage, or discharges to 13.5% of the starting voltage. After three time constants, a capacitor is charged up to 95% of the applied voltage or discharged to 5% of the starting voltage.

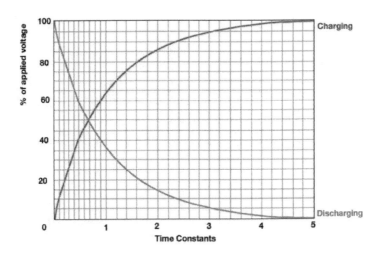

QUESTION: What is the term for the time required for the capacitor in an RC circuit to be charged to 63.2% of the applied voltage or to discharge to 36.8% of its initial voltage? (E5B01)

ANSWER: **One time constant**

QUESTION: What is the time constant of a circuit having

two 220-microfarad capacitors and two 1-megohm resistors, all in parallel? (E5B04)

ANSWER: **220 seconds**

The equivalent resistance of two 1 MΩ resistors in parallel is 500 kΩ. The equivalent capacitance of two 220 μF capacitors in parallel is 440 μF. The time constant is R × C = (440×10^{-6}) × (500×10^{3}) = 220 s.

Phase relationships

In an AC circuit, with only resistors, the voltage and current are in phase. What that means is that the voltage and current change in lock step. When the voltage increases, the current increases. When the voltage decreases, the current decreases.

When there are capacitors and inductors in an AC circuit, however, the phase relationship between the voltage and current changes. Specifically, when an AC voltage is applied to a capacitor, the current begins to change, that is to increase and decrease, a quarter cycle, or 90 degrees, before the voltage changes. We say, therefore, that the current "leads" the voltage by 90 degrees. Conversely, we could also say that the voltage lags the current by 90 degrees. See figure below.

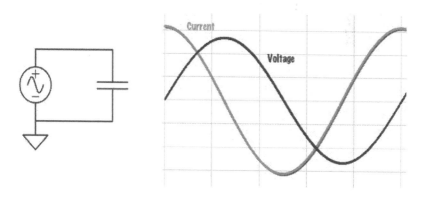

QUESTION: What is the relationship between the AC current through a capacitor and the voltage across a capacitor? (E5B09)

ANSWER: **Current leads voltage by 90 degrees**

The relationship between the current through an inductor and the voltage across an inductor is exactly the opposite. That is to say that the voltage across an inductor increases and decreases before the current through the inductor increases and decreases. In an inductor, the voltage leads the current by a quarter cycle, meaning that the voltage leads current by 90 degrees. We could also say that the current lags the voltage. See figure below.

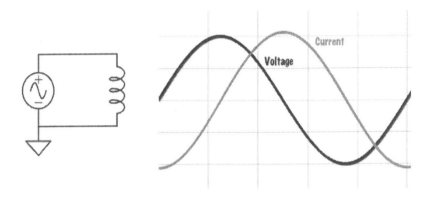

QUESTION: What is the relationship between the AC current through an inductor and the voltage across an inductor? (E5B10)

ANSWER: **Voltage leads current by 90 degrees**

When there are resistors as well as a capacitor or inductor or both in a circuit, the relationship is a little more complicated. Let's look at what happens in the series RLC circuit shown below.

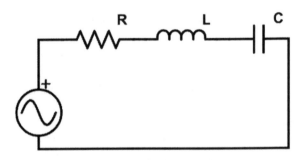

In this circuit, there is resistance, capacitive reactance, and inductive reactance. The reactances subtract from one another. If the capacitive reactance is greater than the inductive reactance, the net reactance will be capacitive. If the inductive reactance is greater than the capacitive reactance, the net reactance will be inductive.

The resistance and reactance add to one another, but they add vectorially. The reason for this is that the reactance will cause the voltage to be out of phase with the current. If the reactance is inductive, the reactance will be positive, as shown in the figure below, the voltage will lead the current, and the phase angle will be a positive value. If the reactance is capacitive, the reactance will be negative, the voltage will lag the current, and the phase angle will be a negative value.

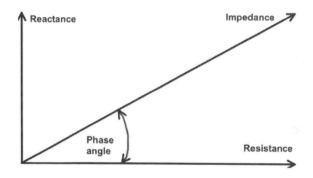

The magnitude of the impedance, Z, will be equal to $\sqrt{(R^2 + X^2)}$ and the tangent of the phase angle will be equal to X/R. Let's see how this works in several examples.

> QUESTION: What is the phase angle between the voltage across and the current through a series RLC circuit if XC is 500 ohms, R is 1 kilohm, and XL is 250 ohms? (E5B07)
>
> ANSWER: **14.0 degrees with the voltage lagging the current**
>
> Here's how to calculate that. First, the total reactance, $X = X_C - X_L = 250\ \Omega$ (capacitive). The phase angle = $\tan^{-1}(250/1000)$

= 14 degrees, and because the reactance is capacitive, the voltage will lag the current.

QUESTION: What is the phase angle between the voltage across and the current through a series RLC circuit if XC is 100 ohms, R is 100 ohms, and XL is 75 ohms? (E5B08)

ANSWER: **14 degrees with the voltage lagging the current**

$X = X_C - X_L = 25 \, \Omega$ (capacitive). The phase angle = $\tan^{-1}$ (25/100) = 14 degrees, and because the reactance is capacitive, the voltage lags the current.

QUESTION: What is the phase angle between the voltage across and the current through a series RLC circuit if XC is 25 ohms, R is 100 ohms, and XL is 50 ohms? (E5B11)

ANSWER: **14 degrees with the voltage leading the current**

$X = X_L - X_C = 25 \, \Omega$ (inductive). The phase angle = $\tan^{-1}$ (25/100) = 14 degrees, and because the reactance is inductive, the voltage leads the current.

Susceptance and admittance

While we most often work with reactances and impedances in amateur radio, in some cases, it's more advantageous to work with susceptance and admittance. Admittance is the inverse of impedance and is a complex quantity. That is to say it has both real and imaginary components. The unit of admittance is the siemens (S).

QUESTION: What is admittance? (E5B12)

ANSWER: **The inverse of impedance**

QUESTION: How is impedance in polar form converted to an equivalent admittance? (E5B03)

ANSWER: **Take the reciprocal of the magnitude and change the sign of the angle**

Susceptance is the imaginary part of admittance, and the unit of susceptance is the siemens. B is the letter commonly used to represent susceptance.

QUESTION: What is susceptance? (E5B06)

ANSWER: **The imaginary part of admittance**

QUESTION: What letter is commonly used to represent susceptance? (E5B02)

ANSWER: **B**

QUESTION: What happens to the magnitude of a pure reactance when it is converted to a susceptance? (E5B05)

ANSWER: **It becomes the reciprocal**

E5C - Impedance plots and coordinate systems: plotting impedances in polar coordinates; rectangular coordinates

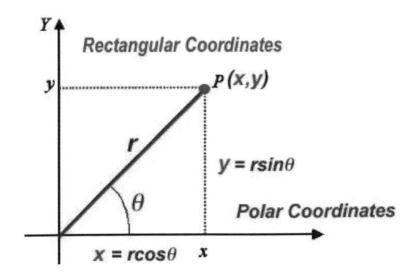

Most often when we plot values on a graph, we use the rectangular, or Cartesian, coordinate system. The two numbers that are used to define a point on a graph using rectangular coordinates are the coordinate values along the horizontal and vertical axes. In the graph above, point P is at x, y.

Rectangular coordinates is the coordinate system often used to display the resistive, inductive, and/or capacitive reactance components of an impedance. When using rectangular coordinates to graph the impedance of a circuit, the X axis, or horizontal axis, represents the resistive component, and the Y axis, or vertical axis, represents the reactive component.

QUESTION: What coordinate system is often used to display the resistive, inductive, and/or capacitive reactance components of impedance? (E5C04)

ANSWER: **Rectangular coordinates**

QUESTION: When using rectangular coordinates to graph the impedance of a circuit, what do the axes represent? (E5C09)

ANSWER: **The X axis represents the resistive component and the Y axis represents the reactive component**

QUESTION: Where is the impedance of a pure resistance plotted on rectangular coordinates? (E5C07)

ANSWER: **On the horizontal axis**

In rectangular notation, we'd represent an impedance as R +/- jX, where X is the value of the reactance. When X is inductive reactance, the reactance is a positive value. When X is negative, the reactance is capacitive.

QUESTION: Which of the following represents capacitive reactance in rectangular notation? (E5C01)

ANSWER: **-jX**

QUESTION: What does the impedance 50-j25 represent? (E5C06)

ANSWER: **50 ohms resistance in series with 25 ohms capacitive reactance**

If the impedance was 50 + j25, then the circuit would have 50 ohms resistance in series with 25 ohm of inductive reactance because +jX represents an inductive reactance.

To figure out the impedance of a circuit, you first plot the inductive reactance on the positive y-axis and the capacitive reactance on the negative y-axis. The net reactance, X, will be the sum of the two reactances. After you've computed the net reactance, you plot the resistance on the x-axis and compute the magnitude of the impedance, shown by r in the graph above. If you consider that r is the third side of a right triangle made up of the sides r, x, and y, r is equal to the square root of $x^2 + y^2$.

When thinking about how capacitive reactances, inductive reactances, and resistances combine in a circuit containing resistors, capacitors, and inductors, it's useful to think in terms of polar coordinates. Polar coordinates show you both the magnitude of an impedance (shown by r in the figure above) and the phase angle of an impedance (shown by θ in the figure above).

QUESTION: What coordinate system is often used to display the phase angle of a circuit containing resistance, inductive and/or capacitive reactance? (E5C08)

ANSWER: **Polar coordinates**

QUESTION: How are impedances described in polar coordinates? (E5C02)

ANSWER: **By phase angle and magnitude**

In polar coordinates, a positive phase angle represents an inductive reactance, and a negative phase angle represents a capacitive reactance. Phasor diagram is the name of the diagram used to show the phase relationship between impedances and resistances at a given frequency.

QUESTION: Which of the following represents an inductive reactance in polar coordinates? (E5C03)

ANSWER: **A positive phase angle**

QUESTION: What is the name of the diagram used to show the phase relationship between impedances at a given frequency? (E5C05)

ANSWER: **Phasor diagram**

Now, let's take a look at some actual circuits.

Figure E5-1

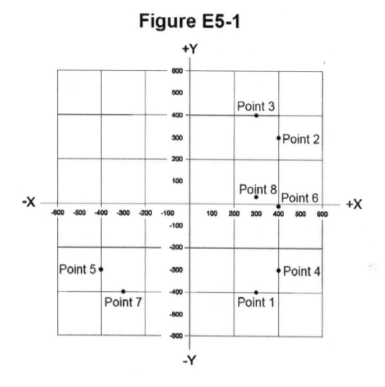

QUESTION: Which point on Figure E5-1 best represents the impedance of a series circuit consisting of a 400-ohm resistor and a 38-picofarad capacitor at 14 MHz? (E5C10)

ANSWER: **Point 4**

Here's how to figure that out. Right off the bat, we know that the only choices are really Points 2, 4, and 6 because the resistance is 400 ohms. Next, we calculate the capacitive reactance:

$$X_C = 1/2\pi fC = 1/(2 \times 3.14 \times 14 \times 10^6 \times 38 \times 10^{-12}) \approx 300 \text{ ohms}$$

Because the reactance is capacitive, it's as a negative value. Point 4 is the only point that has a resistance of 400 ohms a reactance of -300 ohms.

QUESTION: Which point in Figure E5-1 best represents the

impedance of a series circuit consisting of a 300-ohm resistor and an 18-microhenry inductor at 3.505 MHz? (E5C11)

ANSWER: **Point 3**

The resistance for this question is specified to be 300 ohms and the reactance is:

$$X_L = 2\pi fL = 2 \times 3.14 \times 3.505 \times 10^6 \times 18 \times 10^{-6}) \approx 400 \text{ ohms}$$

Because the reactance is inductive, we know it is a positive value. Point 3 is the only point with a resistance of 300 ohms and a reactance of +400 ohms.

QUESTION: Which point on Figure E5-1 best represents the impedance of a series circuit consisting of a 300-ohm resistor and a 19-picofarad capacitor at 21.200 MHz? (E5C12)

ANSWER: **Point 1**

The resistance is 300 ohms, and the reactance is:

$$X_C = 1/2\pi fC = 1/(2 \times 3.14 \times 21.2 \times 10^6 \times 19 \times 10^{-12}) \approx 400 \text{ ohms}$$

Because the reactance is capacitive, it's -400 ohms. Point 1 is the only point with a resistance of 300 ohms and a reactance of -400 ohms.

E5D – AC and RF energy in real circuits: skin effect; electromagnetic fields; reactive power; power factor; electrical length of conductors at UHF and microwave frequencies; microstrip

In AC circuits–and RF circuits are just a type of AC circuit–capacitors and inductors store and release energy as the voltages and currents change. Because of this, calculating power and energy in an AC circuit is not as straightforward as it is for DC circuits.

Capacitors store electrical energy in an electrostatic field. During the positive portion of an AC cycle, the capacitor stores energy in its electrostatic field, but during the negative portion of the cycle, it returns that energy to the circuit.

Inductors store electrical energy in a magnetic field. A similar thing happens to the magnetic field created by the current flow through an inductor that happens to the electrostatic field in a capacitor. When the current flows in one direction, a magnetic field is created. When the current changes direction, the energy stored in that magnetic field gets returned to the circuit.

Conductors, such as wires or traces on printed circuit boards have a small inductance and when current passes through the conductor, it creates a magnetic field around the conductor. The higher the current, the stronger the magnetic field. The magnetic field runs in a circle around the conductor.

> QUESTION: In what direction is the magnetic field oriented about a conductor in relation to the direction of electron flow? (E5D06)
>
> ANSWER: **In a circle around the conductor**

Reactive power

When talking about the power consumed by AC circuits, an important concept is reactive power. Reactive power is often thought of as nonproductive power because it doesn't do any work. During some portions of an AC cycle, inductors and capacitors will draw current and store energy, but during other portions of the cycle, they return that energy to the circuit. The energy is repeatedly exchanged between the magnetic field created by current flowing through the inductors and electric fields in the capacitors, but is not dissipated. The net power dissipation is zero.

QUESTION: What is reactive power? (E5D14)

ANSWER: **Wattless, nonproductive power**

QUESTION: What happens to reactive power in an AC circuit that has both ideal inductors and ideal capacitors? (E5D09)

ANSWER: **It is repeatedly exchanged between the associated magnetic and electric fields, but is not dissipated**

Of course, very few circuits contain only capacitors and inductors. In AC circuits where there is a resistance, that resistance will dissipate real power. Here's an example:

QUESTION: How many watts are consumed in a circuit consisting of a 100-ohm resistor in series with a 100-ohm inductive reactance drawing 1 ampere? (E5D13)

ANSWER: **100 watts**

$P = I^2 \times R = 1A^2 \times 100$ ohms = 100 watts.

This value is called the true power of the circuit because this is the actual amount of power being dissipated by the circuit. But, even though this circuit dissipates 100 watts, it will actually draw more current from a power supply than you would expect because of the inductive reactance. Multiplying this current times the voltage gives you a value called apparent power. The units for apparent power is volt-amperes (VA), to distinguish it from real power. True power is equal to the apparent power multiplied by a value called the power factor of the circuit.

QUESTION: How can the true power be determined in an AC circuit where the voltage and current are out of phase? (E5D10)

ANSWER: **By multiplying the apparent power by the power factor**

QUESTION: How many watts are consumed in a circuit having a power factor of 0.71 if the apparent power is 500VA?

(E5D07)

ANSWER: **355 W**

500 VA x 0.71 = 355 W

The power factor, or PF, is the cosine of the phase angle between the voltage and current. Here are a couple of examples:

QUESTION: What is the power factor of an RL circuit having a 60-degree phase angle between the voltage and the current? (E5D11)

ANSWER: **0.5** (The cosine of 60 degrees is 0.5)

QUESTION: What is the power factor of an RL circuit having a 45-degree phase angle between the voltage and the current? (E5D15)

ANSWER: **0.707** (The cosine of 45 degrees is 0.707)

QUESTION: What is the power factor of an RL circuit having a 30-degree phase angle between the voltage and the current? (E5D05)

ANSWER: **0.866** (The cosine of 30 degrees is 0.866)

Now, let's look at how to calculate the true power dissipated in reactive circuits:

QUESTION: How many watts are consumed in a circuit having a power factor of 0.2 if the input is 100 VAC at 4 amperes? (E5D12)

ANSWER: **80 watts**

The apparent power is 100 VAC x 4 A = 400 VA. True power is apparent power x power factor, or 400 VA x 0.2 = 80 W.

QUESTION: How many watts are consumed in a circuit having a power factor of 0.6 if the input is 200VAC at 5 amperes? (E5D08)

ANSWER: **600 watts**

The apparent power is 200 VAC x 5 A = 1000 VA. True power is apparent power x power or factor, or 1000 VA x 0.6 = 600 W.

The behavior of conductors at high frequencies

At RF frequencies, the current in a conductor tends to flow near the surface of that conductor. As the frequency increases, the current flows in an increasingly thinner layer near the surface of the conductor, and the resistance to the RF current increases. This phenomenon is called the skin effect.

QUESTION: What is the result of skin effect? (E5D01)

ANSWER: **As frequency increases, RF current flows in a thinner layer of the conductor, closer to the surface**

At VHF, UHF, and microwave frequencies, the inductance of conductors must be taken into account. The reason for this is that inductive reactance increases with frequency, and at high frequencies, this reactance is no longer negligible. Because inductance increases with conductor length, it is, important to keep lead lengths short for components used in circuits at VHF frequencies and above.

QUESTION: Why is it important to keep lead lengths short for components used in circuits for VHF and above? (E5D02)

ANSWER: **To avoid unwanted inductive reactance**

Another phenomenon that occurs at high frequencies is that printed circuit board traces begin to act like transmission lines instead of just simple conductors. To properly connect components and circuits, printed circuit board designers carefully lay out the traces so that they run above a ground plane and have a constant impedance.

QUESTION: What is microstrip? (E5D03)

ANSWER: **Precision printed circuit conductors above a ground plane that provide constant impedance interconnects at microwave frequencies**

When designing a printed circuit board that will carry signals at microwave frequencies, it is also import to keep connections as short as possible to prevent signal phase shift.

QUESTION: Why are short connections used at microwave frequencies? (E5D04)

ANSWER: To reduce phase shift along the connection

E6: CIRCUIT COMPONENTS

E6A – Semiconductor materials and devices: semiconductor materials; germanium, silicon, P-type, N-type; transistor types: NPN, PNP, junction, field-effect transistors: enhancement mode; depletion mode; MOS; CMOS; N-channel; P-channel

While transistor theory is outside the scope of this study guide, I will attempt to at least give you a basic understanding of how transistors are put together and how they work. For more information, take a look at these two links:

- How Semiconductors Work (http://www.howstuffworks.com/diode.htm)

- P-type and N-type silicon (http://www.energyresearch.nl/energieopties/zonnecellen/achtergrond/techniek/p-en-n-type-silicium/)

Most transistors we use in amateur radio are made of silicon. Silicon is a semiconductor. That is to say, it's neither a conductor with a very low resistance, like copper, or an insulator with a very high resistance, like plastic or glass.

You can manipulate the electrical characteristics of silicon by adding slight amounts of impurities to a pure silicon crystal. When transistor manufacturers add an impurity that adds free electrons to the silicon crystal, it creates a crystal with a negative charge. We call that type of silicon N-type silicon. When you add other types of impurities to a pure silicon crystal, you can create a crystal with a positive charge. We call this type of material P-type semiconductor material. The majority charge carriers in P-type semiconductor material are called holes.

QUESTION: Which of the following semiconductor

materials contains excess free electrons? (E6A02)

ANSWER: **N-type**

P-type is the type of semiconductor material that contains an excess of holes in the outer shell of electrons. You can think of holes as spots in the crystal that accept free electrons, and the name given to an impurity atom that adds holes to a semiconductor crystal structure is call an acceptor impurity.

QUESTION: What is the name given to an impurity atom that adds holes to a semiconductor crystal structure? (E6A04)

ANSWER: **Acceptor impurity**

Silicon isn't the only semiconductor material used to make transistors. At microwave frequencies, gallium arsenide is used as a semiconductor material in preference to germanium or silicon.

QUESTION: In what application is gallium arsenide used as a semiconductor material? (E6A01)

ANSWER: In microwave circuits

Semiconductor diodes

Diodes are the simplest semiconductor devices. A PN junction diode is formed when you join a bit of P-type material to a bit of N-type material. When you join the two materials, some electrons from the N-type material migrate over to the P-type material and fill holes there. As a result, holes form in the N-type material. This migration of charge forms what is called the depletion region at the PN junction, and an electric field forms across this region. The electric field generates a voltage across the junction.

The most important characteristic of a PN junction diode is that it only allows current to flow when it is forward-biased, that is to say when the voltage applied to the P-type material is more positive than the voltage applied to the N-type material. When a PN junction diode is reversed biased—that is when the voltage applied to the P-type material is more negative than the voltage applied to the N-type material—the diode will not conduct current. A PN-junction diode does not conduct current when reverse biased because holes in P-type material and electrons in the N-type material are separated by the applied voltage, widening the depletion region.

This makes it impossible for current to flow through the region.

QUESTION: Why does a PN-junction diode not conduct current when reverse biased? (E6A03)

ANSWER: **Holes in P-type material and electrons in the N-type material are separated by the applied voltage, widening the depletion region**

Bipolar junction transistors

Perhaps the most popular type of transistor is the bipolar junction transistor (BJT). Bipolar junction transistors have three terminals, called the emitter, base, and collector. In an NPN transistor, the emitter and collector are N-type material and the base is P-type material. In a PNP transistor, the emitter and collector are P-type, while the base is N-type. The base is sandwiched between the collector and emitter, so there is a diode junction between the base and the collector and the base and emitter. The schematic symbols for these transistors are shown below.

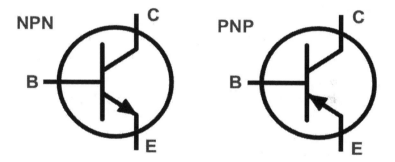

B=base, C=collector, E=emitter

When the base-emitter junction of a silicon NPN junction transistor is forward-biased, a current, called the base current will flow. Since the base-emitter junction is similar to a diode, the voltage across the junction will be approximately 0.6 to 0.7 volts when it is forward biased.

QUESTION: Which of the following indicates that a silicon NPN junction transistor is biased on? (E6A07)

ANSWER: **Base-to-emitter voltage of approximately 0.6 to**

0.7 volts

When a silicon NPN junction transistor is biased on, a small base current will flow, and this base current will cause a much larger current to flow from the collector through the base to the emitter. The amount of base current controls how much collector current flows. This is how transistors amplify signals.

The beta of a bipolar junction transistor, also sometimes called the hfe, or current gain, of a transistor is the ratio of the collector current to the base current.

> QUESTION: What is the beta of a bipolar junction transistor? (E6A06)
>
> ANSWER: **The change in collector current with respect to base current**

Another important characteristic of a bipolar transistor is the alpha cutoff frequency. This is a measure of how high in frequency a transistor will operate. It is the frequency at which the grounded-base current gain of a transistor has decreased to 0.7 of the gain obtainable at 1 kHz

> QUESTION: What term indicates the frequency at which the grounded-base current gain of a transistor has decreased to 0.7 of the gain obtainable at 1 kHz? (E6A08)
>
> ANSWER: **Alpha cutoff frequency**

Field effect transistors

A field-effect transistor (FET) is a device that uses an electric field to control current flow through the device. Like the bipolar transistor, a FET normally has three terminals. The names of the three terminals of a field-effect transistor are gate (G), drain (D), and source (S). Just like a bipolar junction transistor is made with P-type and N-type semiconductor material, so is a FET. There are many different types of FETS, depending on how they are made. Figure E6-1 shows the schematic symbols for six different types, including the P-channel junction FET (#1) and the N-channel dual-gate MOSFET (#4).

Figure E6-1

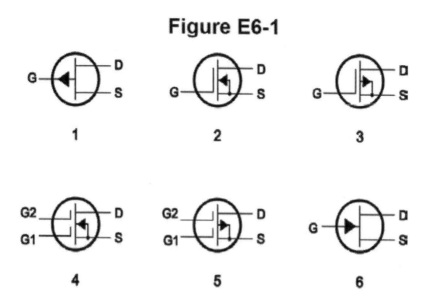

QUESTION: In Figure E6-1, what is the schematic symbol for an N-channel dual-gate MOSFET? (E6A10)

ANSWER: **4**

QUESTION: In Figure E6-1, what is the schematic symbol for a P-channel junction FET? (E6A11)

ANSWER: **1**

One characteristic of MOSFETs is that they have a high input impedance when compared to bipolar transistors. This makes them more attractive than bipolar transistors in many test equipment applications because they don't provide much of a load to the circuit under test. One disadvantage of using MOSFETs is that they are very sensitive to electrostatic discharge (ESD). Sometimes, they are damaged by static discharges so low that you never even see the spark or feel the shock. To reduce the sensitivity to ESD, many MOSFET devices have internally connected Zener diodes on the gates.

QUESTION: How does DC input impedance at the gate of a field-effect transistor compare with the DC input impedance of a bipolar transistor? (E6A05)

ANSWER: **An FET has higher input impedance**

QUESTION: Why do many MOSFET devices have internally connected Zener diodes on the gates? (E6A12)

ANSWER: **To reduce the chance of static damage to the gate**

Most FETs are enhancement-mode devices. When using an enhancement-mode FET, you must apply a voltage to the gate to get current to flow from source to drain. Some FETs are, however, depletion mode devices. A depletion-mode FET allows current to flow between source and drain when no gate voltage is applied.

QUESTION: What is a depletion-mode FET? (E6A09)

ANSWER: **An FET that exhibits a current flow between source and drain when no gate voltage is applied**

E6B – Diodes

Diodes have two terminals and conduct current in only one direction, from the cathode to the anode. By manipulating the characteristics of the semiconductor material, manufacturers can make diodes useful in a wide variety of applications.

Take, for example, the Zener diode. Zener diodes actually allow current to flow in both directions, but only when the reverse bias voltage reaches a specific voltage, called the Zener voltage. When the voltage across the Zener diode reaches that point, it begins to conduct current in the reverse direction and maintains a constant voltage drop across the diode. This makes it useful in voltage regulator circuits.

QUESTION: What is the most useful characteristic of a Zener diode? (E6B01)

ANSWER: **A constant voltage drop under conditions of varying current**

Another example is the varactor diode. The capacitance of a varactor diodes changes as you change the voltage across it. This allows you to use it as a voltage-controlled capacitor in tuning circuits.

QUESTION: What type of semiconductor device is designed for use as a voltage-controlled capacitor? (E6B04)

ANSWER: **Varactor diode**

PIN diodes are diodes that operate as a variable resistor at RF and microwave frequencies. One common use for PIN diodes is as an RF switch. One characteristic of a PIN diode that makes it useful as an RF switch or attenuator is low junction capacitance. The forward DC bias current level is used to control the attenuation of RF signals by a PIN diode.

QUESTION: What characteristic of a PIN diode makes it useful as an RF switch? (E6B05)

ANSWER: **Low junction capacitance**

QUESTION: What is used to control the attenuation of RF signals by a PIN diode? (E6B11)

ANSWER: **Forward DC bias current**

Schottky diodes have a metal-semiconductor junction and have less forward voltage drop than other types of diodes. For this reason, they are often used as a power supply rectifier. They are also often used as a VHF/UHF mixer or detector. When used in digital ICs, the Schottky diode's lower forward voltage drop allow the ICs to switch faster.

QUESTION: What is an important characteristic of a Schottky diode as compared to an ordinary silicon diode when used as a power supply rectifier? (E6B02)

ANSWER: **Less forward voltage drop**

QUESTION: Which of the following is a common use of a Schottky diode? (E6B06)

ANSWER: **As a VHF/UHF mixer or detector**

QUESTION: Which of the following is a Schottky barrier diode? (E6B08)

ANSWER: Metal-semiconductor junction

Point-contact diodes are commonly used as RF detectors.

QUESTION: What is a common use for point-contact diodes? (E6B09)

ANSWER: **As an RF detector**

Light-emitting diodes, or LEDs, are widely used in amateur radio as visual indicators. When you forward bias an LED, current flows through the diode and it emits light. The schematic symbol for an LED is similar to the symbol for a signal diode, but has two arrows pointing away from the diode that are meant to show that it is emitting light.

QUESTION: What type of bias is required for an LED to emit light? (E6B03)

ANSWER: **Forward bias**

QUESTION: In Figure E6-2, what is the schematic symbol for a light-emitting diode? (E6B10)

ANSWER: **5**

Figure E6-2

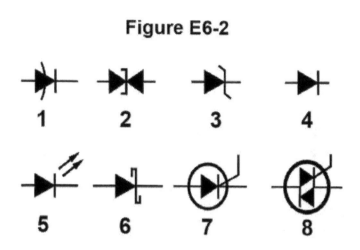

No matter what type of diode you are using, it's very important to not exceed the forward current specification. Doing so, will cause the junction temperature to increase, and ultimately cause the diode to fail.

QUESTION: What is the failure mechanism when a junction diode fails due to excessive current? (E6B07)

ANSWER: **Excessive junction temperature**

E6C – Digital ICs: Families of digital ICs; gates; Programmable Logic Devices (PLDs)

Integrated circuits (ICs) are now an integral part (pun intended) of amateur radio electronics. There are several different technologies used to manufacture ICs including transistor-transistor logic, or TTL; complementary metal-oxide semiconductor, or CMOS; and BiCMOS, which uses a combination of bipolar and CMOS transistors.

CMOS is arguably the most common type of digital IC. One of the reasons for this is that CMOS logic devices consume less power than TTL devices. They also are more immune to power supply noise and noise on the inputs because the input switching threshold is about one-half the power supply voltage.

> QUESTION: What is an advantage of CMOS logic devices over TTL devices? (E6C05)
>
> ANSWER: **Lower power consumption**
>
> QUESTION: Why do CMOS digital integrated circuits have high immunity to noise on the input signal or power supply? (E6C06)
>
> ANSWER: **The input switching threshold is about one-half the power supply voltage**

BiCMOS logic is an integrated circuit logic family that uses both bipolar and CMOS transistors. An advantage of BiCMOS logic is that it has the high input impedance of CMOS and the low output impedance of bipolar transistors.

> QUESTION: Which of the following is an advantage of BiCMOS logic? (E6C04)
>
> ANSWER: **It has the high input impedance of CMOS and the low output impedance of bipolar transistors**

Some devices have three different output states: 0, 1, and a high-impedance state. We call these devices tri-state logic devices. The high-impedance state allows you to connect many of them to a common bus. When a device's outputs are in the high-impedance state, they act as if they are disconnected.

QUESTION: What is tri-state logic? (E6C03)

ANSWER: **Logic devices with 0, 1, and high-impedance output states**

Figure E6-3

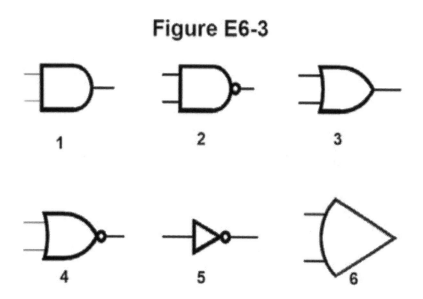

When working with digital ICs, it is important to recognize the various symbols for the different types of logic gates. Figure E6-3 shows the schematic symbols for the most common logic gates. It includes the following:

1. AND gate
2. NAND gate
3. OR gate
4. NOR gate
5. NOT (inverter)
6. Not a valid logic gate symbol.

QUESTION: In Figure E6-3, what is the schematic symbol for a NAND gate? (E6C08)

ANSWER: **2**

QUESTION: In Figure E6-3, what is the schematic symbol

for a NOR gate? (E6C10)

ANSWER: **4**

QUESTION: In Figure E6-3, what is the schematic symbol for the NOT operation (inverter)? (E6C11)

ANSWER: **5**

When designing circuits with digital ICs, you may not use all of the inputs of the gates in that IC. To set that input to a digital 1 or 0, you might use a pull-up resistor or a pull-down resistor. A pull-up would be connected to the positive supply line while a pull-down would be normally connected to ground. Pull-up resistors are also often used on the output of a digital circuit to prevent the output from floating.

QUESTION: What best describes a pull-up or pull-down resistor? (E6C07)

ANSWER: **A resistor connected to the positive or negative supply line used to establish a voltage when an input or output is an open circuit**

A comparator is an IC that compares an input voltage to a threshold voltage, and when the level of the input signal crosses the threshold, the comparator changes its output state.

Comparators have a property called hysteresis. Basically, what this means is that the threshold voltage is lower when the input voltage is decreasing than the threshold voltage when the input voltage is increasing. The function of hysteresis in a comparator is to prevent input noise from causing unstable output signals. If the threshold voltage was the same for both increasing and decreasing input voltages, and the input voltage was right at the threshold voltage, then noise could cause that input voltage to go above and below the threshold randomly. If the comparator input did not have hysteresis, then its output would switch randomly.

QUESTION: What happens when the level of a comparator's input signal crosses the threshold? (E6C02)

ANSWER: **The comparator changes its output state**

QUESTION: What is the function of hysteresis in a comparator? (E6C01)

ANSWER: **To prevent input noise from causing unstable output signals**

Many modern electronic devices now use programmable logic devices instead of cobbling together a digital circuit with a collection of ICs with simple gates. A Programmable Logic Device (PLD) is an integrated circuit that has a collection of logic gates and circuits that you can connect in different ways. Programmable logic devices can have thousands or even millions of gates in a single IC. To design digital circuits with PLDs, designers use computer-aided design software to connect and configure the logic gates.

QUESTION: What is a Programmable Logic Device (PLD)? (E6C09)

ANSWER: **A programmable collection of logic gates and circuits in a single integrated circuit**

E6D – Toroidal and solenoidal Inductors: permeability, core material, selecting, winding; transformers; piezoelectric devices

Solenoidal and toroidal inductors are both used in amateur radio equipment. A solenoidal inductor is a coil of wire wound around a cylindrical core, while a toroidal inductor is a coil of wire wound around a circular or toroidal core. Solenoidal inductors often have just an air core, while toroidal inductors are wound around a ferrite or powdered-iron core.

The primary advantage of using a toroidal core inductor is that the core confines the magnetic field within the core material, meaning that there's less chance of unwanted mutual induction. Another advantage is that they are more compact than solenoidal inductors with the same inductance. The characteristic of a toroid core that determines the inductance of a toroidal inductor is its permeability.

QUESTION: What is a primary advantage of using a toroidal core instead of a solenoidal core in an inductor? (E6D10)

ANSWER: **Toroidal cores confine most of the magnetic field within the core material**

QUESTION: What core material property determines the inductance of an inductor? (E6D06)

ANSWER: **Permeability**

There are two types of toroidal cores commonly used in amateur radio equipment: powdered-iron cores and ferrite cores. One reason for using powdered-iron toroids rather than ferrite toroids in an inductor is that powdered-iron toroids generally maintain their characteristics at higher currents. One reason for using ferrite toroids rather than powdered-iron toroids in an inductor is that ferrite toroids generally require fewer turns to produce a given inductance value. This characteristic makes ferrite beads a good choice for use as VHF and UHF parasitic suppressors at the input and output terminals of transistorized HF amplifiers.

QUESTION: What is one reason for using powdered-iron cores rather than ferrite cores in an inductor? (E6D08)

ANSWER: **Powdered-iron cores generally maintain their characteristics at higher currents**

QUESTION: What is one reason for using ferrite cores rather than powdered iron in an inductor? (E6D05)

ANSWER: **Ferrite toroids generally require fewer turns to produce a given inductance value**

QUESTION: What devices are commonly used as VHF and UHF parasitic suppressors at the input and output terminals of a transistor HF amplifier? (E6D09)

ANSWERS: **Ferrite beads**

When designing circuits with ferrite-core inductors, you have to be careful not to saturate the core. Saturating the core means that you have exceeded the ability of the core to store magnetic energy. Saturating the core of a toroidal inductor can cause it to change inductance and increase losses.

QUESTION: What is inductor saturation? (E6D12)

ANSWER: **The ability of the inductor's core to store magnetic energy has been exceeded**

One problem that may occur in a circuit with inductors is self-resonance. At some frequency, also called the "self-resonant frequency," inter-turn capacitance forms a parallel resonant circuit with the inductor.

QUESTION: What is the primary cause of inductor self-resonance? (E6D13)

ANSWER: **Inter-turn capacitance**

Variable inductors are made by inserting a slug, generally either ferrite or brass, into an air-core inductor. By varying the position of the slug, you vary the inductance. A brass slug decreases inductance when inserted into a coil.

QUESTION: Which materials are commonly used as a core in an inductor? (E6D04)

ANSWER: **Ferrite and brass**

QUESTION: Which type of core material decreases

inductance when inserted into a coil? (E6D11)

ANSWER: **Brass**

Transformers

A transformer consists of two inductors that are closely coupled. Connecting an AC voltage across one of the inductors, called the primary winding, causes a current to flow in the primary, which then generates a magnetic field. As the lines of this field cross the turns of the secondary winding, it induces a current to flow in the secondary, and the voltage across the secondary is equal to the voltage across the primary winding times the number of turns in the secondary winding divided by the number of turns in the primary winding. The current in the primary winding of a transformer is called the magnetizing current if no load is attached to the secondary.

Transformers are often used to match the output impedance of one circuit to the input impedance of another. In this application, it's important not to saturate the core of the transformer. Saturating the core of a conventional impedance matching transformer should be avoided because doing so could create harmonics and distort the signal.

QUESTION: What is current in the primary winding of a transformer called if no load is attached to the secondary? (E6D07)

ANSWER: **Magnetizing current**

QUESTION: Why should core saturation of an impedance matching transformer be avoided? (E6D01)

ANSWER: **Harmonics and distortion could result**

Piezoelectric devices

Piezoelectric crystals are used in many amateur radio applications, including oscillators and filters. They are called piezoelectric crystals because they rely on the piezoelectric effect, which is the physical deformation of a crystal by the application of a voltage. The equivalent circuit of a quartz crystal is a capacitance, inductance, and resistance in series, all in parallel with a shunt capacitor representing electrode and stray capacitance.

QUESTION: Which of the following is an aspect of the

piezoelectric effect? (E6D03)

ANSWER: **Mechanical deformation of material by the application of a voltage**

QUESTION: What is the equivalent circuit of a quartz crystal? (E6D02)

ANSWER: **Motional capacitance, motional inductance, and loss resistance in series, all in parallel with a shunt capacitor representing electrode and stray capacitance**

E6E Analog ICs: MMICs, IC packaging characteristics

Monolithic microwave integrated circuits, or MMICs, are ICs that are made to perform various functions at high frequencies. MMICs have:
- Controlled gain.
- Low noise figure (VHF and UHF preamplifiers have a noise figure typically 2 dB or less).
- Constant input and output impedance (50 Ω, of course, for RF circuits) over the specified frequency range.

These features make them a popular choice for high-frequency circuits, from VHF through microwave.

QUESTION: What characteristics of the MMIC make it a popular choice for VHF through microwave circuits? (E6E06)

ANSWER: **Controlled gain, low noise figure, and constant input and output impedance over the specified frequency range**

QUESTION: Which of the following noise figure values is typical of a low-noise UHF preamplifier? (E6E05)

ANSWER: **2 dB**

QUESTION: Which is the most common input and output impedance of circuits that use MMICs? (E6E04)

ANSWER: **50 ohms**

MMICs are often made from the semiconductor gallium nitride because it is the material most likely to provide the highest frequency of operation. Another semiconductor that is used for devices operating at UHF and higher frequencies is gallium arsenide (GaAs). One reason for this is that it has higher electron mobility than silicon.

QUESTION: Which of the following materials is likely to provide the highest frequency of operation when used in MMICs? (E6E03)

ANSWER: **Gallium nitride**

QUESTION: Why is gallium arsenide (GaAs) useful for semiconductor devices operating at UHF and higher frequencies? (E6E01)

ANSWER: **Higher electron mobility**

To achieve these specifications, great care is taken in building and using circuits that use MMICs. For example, MMIC-based microwave amplifiers use microstrip construction to connect to the integrated circuit. To prevent RF from getting into the power supply, power is connected to an MMIC through a resistor and/or RF choke connected to the amplifier output lead.

QUESTION: What type of transmission line is used for connections to MMICs? (E6E07)

ANSWER: **Microstrip**

QUESTION: How is power supplied to the most common type of MMIC? (E6E08)

ANSWER: **Through a resistor and/or RF choke connected to the amplifier output lead**

Device packages

Integrated circuits come in many different types of packages. One of the most common packages for an integrated circuit is the dual-inline package, or DIP. DIPs have two rows of connecting pins placed on opposite sides of the package. Because a DIP's pins are made to fit into the holes on a printed-circuit board and extend through that board, it is called a "through-hole" type.

QUESTION: What is a characteristic of DIP packaging used for integrated circuits? (E6E11)

ANSWER: **A total of two rows of connecting pins placed on opposite sides of the package (Dual In-line Package)**

QUESTION: Which of the following device packages is a through-hole type? (E6E02)

ANSWER: **DIP**

For a variety of reasons, electronics companies are moving away from ICs in through-hole, dual inline packages and moving towards surface-mount packages. One reason for this is excessive lead length. ICs in surface mount packages are leadless and soldered directly to circuit boards. They offer a number of advantages, including:

- Smaller package sizes, which means printed circuit boards are smaller.
- Shorter circuit board traces.
- Less parasitic inductance and capacitance, which makes their performance at high frequencies more predictable.

QUESTION: Why are DIP through-hole package ICs not typically used at UHF and higher frequencies? (E6E12)

ANSWER: **Excessive lead length**

QUESTION: Which of the following component package types would be most suitable for use at frequencies above the HF range? (E6E09)

ANSWER: **Surface mount**

QUESTION: What advantage does surface-mount technology offer at RF compared to using through-hole components? (E6E10)

ANSWER: **All these choices are correct**

○ Smaller circuit area

○ Shorter circuit-board traces

○ Components have less parasitic inductance and capacitance

E6F: Electro-optical technology: photoconductivity; photovoltaic devices; optical sensors and encoders; optical isolation

Some components make use of the photovoltaic effect, which is the process of converting light to electrical energy. In a photovoltaic cell, electrons absorb the energy from light falling on a photovoltaic cell. The electrons then become free electrons.

QUESTION: What is the photovoltaic effect? (E6F04)

ANSWER: **The conversion of light to electrical energy**

QUESTION: What absorbs the energy from light falling on a photovoltaic cell? (E6F01)

ANSWER: **Electrons**

The most common type of photovoltaic cell used for electrical power generation is made from silicon, and the approximate open-circuit voltage produced by a fully-illuminated silicon photovoltaic cell is 0.5 V.

The efficiency of a photovoltaic cell is the relative fraction of light that is converted to current. In recent years, manufacturers have greatly increased the efficiency of their solar panels, making solar power feasible for many amateur radio applications.

QUESTION: What is the most common type of photovoltaic cell used for electrical power generation? (E6F10)

ANSWER: **Silicon**

QUESTION: What is the approximate open-circuit voltage produced by a fully illuminated silicon photovoltaic cell? (E6F11)

ANSWER: **0.5 V**

QUESTION: What is the efficiency of a photovoltaic cell? (E6F09)

ANSWER: **The relative fraction of light that is converted to current**

Photoconductivity is a similar phenomenon. The conductivity of a photoconductive material increases when light shines on it, allowing you to use it as a sensor. Crystalline semiconductors are the most commonly-used materials for making photoconductive devices.

QUESTION: What happens to the conductivity of a photoconductive material when light shines on it? (E6F02)

ANSWER: **It increases**

QUESTION: Which of these materials is most commonly used to create photoconductive devices? (E6F06)

ANSWER: **A crystalline semiconductor**

A device that uses the phenomenon of photoconductivity is the optoisolator. Optoisolators and optocouplers consist of an an LED and a phototransistor. A current flowing through the LED causes it to emit light, which then turns on the phototransistor. These components provide electrical isolation because LED and the phototransistor are separated by a small gap and there is no electrical connection between them. Optoisolators are often used in conjunction with solid state circuits when switching 120 VAC because optoisolators provide a very high degree of electrical isolation between a control circuit and the circuit being switched.

QUESTION: What is the most common configuration of an optoisolator or optocoupler? (E6F03)

ANSWER: **An LED and a phototransistor**

QUESTION: Why are optoisolators often used in conjunction with solid-state circuits when switching 120 VAC? (E6F08)

ANSWER: **Optoisolators provide a very high degree of electrical isolation between a control circuit and the circuit being switched**

A similar device is the solid-state relay. A solid state relay is a circuit that acts like a relay, but uses semiconductor devices instead of a mechanical switch. To provide the electrical isolation normally provided by a mechanical relay, a solid state relay might use an optocoupler.

QUESTION: What is a solid-state relay? (E6F07)

ANSWER: **A device that uses semiconductors to implement the functions of an electromechanical relay**

An optical shaft encoder is another device that relies on photoconductivity. It consists of a light source, a phototransistor, and a patterned wheel. As the wheel rotates between the light source and the photo transistor, it interrupts the light source, causing the phototransistor to turn on and off. The resulting output allows a microcontroller to detect when the shaft is rotating and in which direction. One application for an optical shaft encoder is to allow a radio to detect when an operator is turning a knob.

QUESTION: Which describes an optical shaft encoder? (E6F05)

ANSWER: **A device that detects rotation of a control by interrupting a light source with a patterned wheel**

E7: PRACTICAL CIRCUITS

E7A – Digital circuits: digital circuit principles and logic circuits; classes of logic elements; positive and negative logic; frequency dividers; truth tables

Digital circuits are used for a variety of functions in modern amateur radio equipment. Unlike analog circuits, the output voltage of an ideal digital circuit can only be one of two values. One of these voltages—normally a positive voltage—represents a digital 1. The other value—normally near 0 V —represents a digital 0. This type of logic is called positive logic. On the other hand, some digital logic systems use a low voltage to represent a digital 1 and a high voltage to represent a digital 0. This type of logic is called negative logic.

> QUESTION: What type of logic defines "1" as a high voltage?
> (E7A11)
>
> ANSWER: **Positive Logic**

The microcomputers that control today's transceivers are very complex digital circuits. These complex digital circuits are made by combining many smaller building blocks called logic gates. These gates perform basic digital logic functions.

One of the most basic digital circuits is the NAND gate. The output of a NAND gate is a logic 0 when all of its inputs are a logic 1. Truth tables describe how logic gates work. That is to say that they show what the logic gate output is for each combination of inputs. Table E7-1 shows a truth table that describes the operation of a two-input NAND gate. A and B are the two inputs; Q is the output.

2-INPUT NAND		
A	B	Q
0	0	1
0	1	1
1	0	1
1	1	0

Table E7-1

QUESTION: What logical operation does a NAND gate perform? (E7A07)

ANSWER: **It produces logic 0 at its output only when all inputs are logic 1**

QUESTION: What is a truth table? (E7A10)

ANSWER: **A list of inputs and corresponding outputs for a digital device**

Other types of gates perform different logical functions. OR gates, for example, output a logic 1 if any or all of its inputs are a logic 1. Table E7-2 shows a truth table that describes the logical operation of a two-input OR gate.

2-INPUT OR		
A	B	Q
0	0	0
0	1	1
1	0	1
1	1	1

Table E7-2

QUESTION: What logical operation does an OR gate perform? (E7A08)

ANSWER: **It produces logic 1 at its output if any or all inputs are logic 1**

A NOR gate produces exactly the opposite output of an OR gate. That is to say that the output is a logic 0 if any or all of the inputs are a logic 1. An exclusive NOR (XNOR) gate is similar to the NOR gate, except that its output is a logic 0 when its inputs are not all the same value. If all the inputs are a logic 1 or a logic 0, the XNOR gate will output a logic 1 as shown in Table E7-3, which is a truth table for a two-input XNOR gate.

2-INPUT XNOR		
A	B	Q
0	0	1
0	1	0
1	0	0
1	1	1

Table E7-3

QUESTION: What logical operation is performed by an exclusive NOR gate? (E7A09)

ANSWER: **It produces logic 0 at its output if only one input is logic 1**

Flip-flops are circuits that are made from combinations of logic gates. By "latching" the state of an input at a particular time, a flip-flop can be said to have memory. A D flip-flop, and its truth table is shown in the figure below.

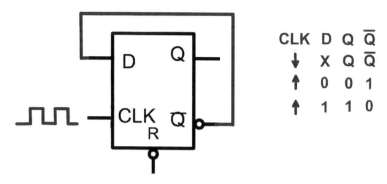

D flip-flop and truth table.

As shown, the output changes only on the rising edge of the clock (CLK) signal. That is to say, when the signal goes from 0 to 1. If D = 1, Q = 1. If D = 0, then Q = 0. The other output, denoted by a bar over the Q, is the inverse of Q.

When a D flip-flop is connected as shown in the figure—with the inverted output connected to the D input—a flip-flop can divide the frequency of a pulse train by 2. You can connect the Q output to a second flip-flop to divide the frequency even further. Consequently, 2 flip-flops are required to divide a signal frequency by 4. By connecting a number of flip-flops together, and resetting the circuit once ten pulses have been input, you can build a decade counter.

> QUESTION: Which of the following can divide the frequency of a pulse train by 2? (E7A03)
>
> ANSWER: **A flip-flop**
>
> QUESTION: How many flip-flops are required to divide a signal frequency by 4? (E7A04)
>
> ANSWER: **2**
>
> QUESTION: What is the function of a decade counter? (E7A02)
>
> ANSWER: **It produces one output pulse for every 10 input pulses**

A flip-flop is a bistable circuit. That means its output is stable in either state

—1 or 0. Some circuits—called monostable circuits—are stable in only one state, but not the other. They will switch from one state to the other, but then return to the original state. One such monostable circuit is the monostable multivibrator. A trigger pulse causes the monostable vibrator to switch from a 1 to a 0 (or vice versa), but after a set time, the output of the monostable vibrator will return to its original state. An astable multivibrator is not stable in either state. Its output continuously alternates between two states without an external clock. In other words, it is an oscillator.

QUESTION: Which circuit is bistable? (E7A01)

ANSWER: **A flip-flop**

QUESTION: What is a characteristic of a monostable multivibrator? (E7A06)

ANSWER: **It switches momentarily to the opposite binary state and then returns to its original state after a set time**

QUESTION: Which of the following is a circuit that continuously alternates between two states without an external clock? (E7A05)

ANSWER: **Astable multivibrator**

E7B – Amplifiers class of operation; vacuum tube and solid-state circuits; distortion and intermodulation; spurious and parasitic suppression; microwave amplifiers; switching-type amplifiers

There are several classes of amplifiers, based on their mode of operation. In a class A amplifier, the transistor is always conducting current. Because the transistor is always conducting current, the bias of a Class A common emitter amplifier would normally be set approximately halfway between saturation and cutoff on the load line.

> QUESTION: Where on the load line of a Class A common emitter amplifier would bias normally be set? (E7B04)
>
> ANSWER: **Approximately halfway between saturation and cutoff**

In a class B amplifier, there are normally two transistors operating in a "push-pull" configuration. One transistor turns on during the positive half of a cycle, while the other turns on during the negative half. One advantage of using push-pull amplifiers is that they reduce even-order harmonics.

> QUESTION: Which of the following amplifier types reduces even-order harmonics? (E7B06)
>
> ANSWER: **Push-pull**

A Class AB amplifier operates over more than 180 degrees but less than 360 degrees of a signal cycle. Class B and Class AB amplifiers are more efficient than Class A amplifiers.

> QUESTION: For what portion of the signal cycle does each active element in a push-pull Class AB amplifier conduct? (E7B01)
>
> ANSWER: **More than 180 degrees but less than 360 degrees**

Class C amplifiers conduct over less than 180 degrees of the input signal.

This type of operation distorts the output signal, but it is very efficient. Up to 90% efficiency is possible.

A Class D amplifier uses switching technology to achieve high efficiency. They are very efficient because the power transistor is at cutoff or near saturation most of time. To remove switching signal components, the output of a class D amplifier circuit has a low-pass filter.

QUESTION: What is a Class D amplifier? (E7B02)

ANSWER: **A type of amplifier that uses switching technology to achieve high efficiency**

QUESTION: Why are switching amplifiers more efficient than linear amplifiers? (E7B14)

ANSWER: **The power transistor is at saturation or cutoff most of the time**

QUESTION: Which of the following components form the output of a class D amplifier circuit? (E7B03)

ANSWER: **A low-pass filter to remove switching signal components**

Amplifiers are used in many different applications, and in most signal quality is very important. Poorly-designed RF power amplifiers, for example, may emit harmonics or spurious signals, that may cause harmful interference.

One thing that can be done to prevent unwanted oscillations—that can generate harmonics or spurious emissions—in an RF power amplifier is to install parasitic suppressors or neutralize the stage. To neutralize an RF power amplifier, you feed a portion of the output back to the input, but shift the phase 180 degrees. Doing this will eliminate the effects of any parasitic capacitance or inductance that might cause an amplifier to oscillate.

QUESTION: What can be done to prevent unwanted oscillations in an RF power amplifier? (E7B05)

ANSWER: **Install parasitic suppressors and/or neutralize the stage**

QUESTION: How can an RF power amplifier be neutralized? (E7B08)

ANSWER: **By feeding a 180-degree out-of-phase portion of the output back to the input**

In order to preserve signal integrity, amplifiers used as the final amplifier in an amateur radio transceiver, or as an external amplifier, are Class A or Class AB linear amplifiers. The use of non-linear Class C amplifiers is not a good choice. The reason for this that a Class C amplifier used to amplify a single-sideband phone signal can cause signal distortion and excessive bandwidth.

QUESTION: Which of the following is a likely result when a Class C amplifier is used to amplify a single-sideband phone signal? (E7B07)

ANSWER: **Signal distortion and excessive bandwidth**

Although transistorized linear amplifiers are becoming more common, many high-power amplifiers still use vacuum tubes. These amplifiers require that the operator tune the output circuit, which is typically a Pi-network output circuit. To tune this type of output circuit, you adjust the tuning capacitor for minimum plate current and the loading capacitor for maximum permissible plate current.

QUESTION: Which of the following describes how the loading and tuning capacitors are to be adjusted when tuning a vacuum tube RF power amplifier that employs a Pi-network output circuit? (E7B09)

ANSWER: **The tuning capacitor is adjusted for minimum plate current, and the loading capacitor is adjusted for maximum permissible plate current**

Figure E7-1

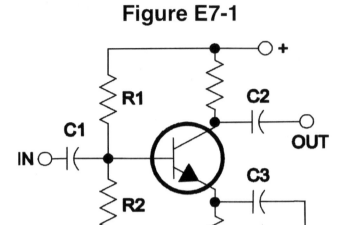

The type of circuit shown in Figure E7-1 is a common emitter amplifier. R1 and R2 bias the transistor. This type of bias is called voltage divider bias. R3 also sets the bias voltages for the transistor. The type of bias provided by R3 is called self bias.

QUESTION: What type of amplifier circuit is shown in Figure E7-1? (E7B12)

ANSWER: **Common emitter**

QUESTION: In Figure E7-1, what is the purpose of R1 and R2? (E7B10)

ANSWER: **Voltage divider bias**

QUESTION: In Figure E7-1, what is the purpose of R3? (E7B11)

ANSWER: **Self bias**

Another type of amplifier circuit is the emitter follower, or common collector amplifier. These types of amplifiers are often used as buffer amplifiers because they have low-impedance outputs that closely follow the base input voltage.

QUESTION: Which of the following describes an emitter follower (or common collector) amplifier? (E7B13)

ANSWER: **An amplifier with a low impedance output that follows the base input voltage**

Thermal runaway is one problem that can occur if a transistor amplifier is not designed correctly. What happens is that when the ambient temperature increases, the leakage current of the transistor increases, causing an increase in the collector-to-emitter current. This increases the power dissipation, further increasing the junction temperature, which increases yet again the leakage current. One way to prevent thermal runaway in a bipolar transistor amplifier is to use a resistor in series with the emitter. This resistor keeps the collector-to-emitter current under control.

QUESTION: What is one way to prevent thermal runaway in a bipolar transistor amplifier? (E7B15)

ANSWER: **Use a resistor in series with the emitter**

RF power amplifiers often generate unwanted signals via a process called intermodulation. Strong signals external to the transmitter combine with the signal being generated. These intermodulation products can cause the transmitter to output spurious signals. Odd-order, rather than even-order, intermodulation distortion products are of concern in linear power amplifiers because they are relatively close in frequency to the desired signal.

QUESTION: What is the effect of intermodulation products in a linear power amplifier? (E7B16)

ANSWER: **Transmission of spurious signals**

QUESTION: Why are odd-order rather than even-order intermodulation distortion products of concern in linear power amplifiers? (E7B17)

ANSWER: **Because they are relatively close in frequency to the desired signal**

One type of amplifier that is often used as a power amplifier is the grounded-grid amplifier. Grounded-grid amplifiers are relatively easy to build, are very stable in operation, and have a low input impedance. This is a useful characteristic because the output impedance of most amateur radio transmitters, which are used to drive these amplifiers, is 50 ohms.

QUESTION: What is a characteristic of a grounded-grid amplifier? (E7B18)

ANSWER: **Low input impedance**

E7C – Filters and matching networks: types of networks; types of filters; filter applications; filter characteristics; impedance matching; DSP filtering

Because the impedance of inductors and capacitors vary with frequency, we often make filters out of them. One of the most common is the T-network filter, so called because it looks like the letter T. An example is shown in figure E7C-1.

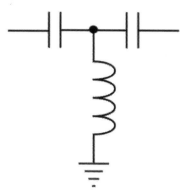

Figure E7C-1. T-network filter

This particular filter is a T-network high-pass filter. That is to say it will pass frequencies above a certain frequency, called the cutoff frequency, and block frequencies below that frequency. The reason the circuit acts this way is that as the frequency of a signal increases, capacitive reactance decreases and inductive reactance increases, meaning that lower-frequency signals are more likely to be shunted to ground.

> QUESTION: Which of the following is a property of a T-network with series capacitors and a parallel shunt inductor? (E7C02)
>
> ANSWER: **It is a high-pass filter**

A circuit containing capacitors and inductors can also form a low-pass filter. A low-pass filter is a circuit that passes frequencies below the cutoff frequency and blocks frequencies above it. The circuit shown in figure E7C-2 is called a low-pass, pi filter because it looks like the Greek letter π. The capacitors and inductors of a low-pass filter Pi-network are arranged such that a capacitor is connected between the input and ground, another capacitor is connected between the output and ground, and an inductor is connected between input and output. The reason the circuit acts as a low-pass filter is that as the frequency of a signal increases, capacitive reactance decreases and inductive reactance increases, meaning that higher-frequency signals are more likely to be shunted to ground.

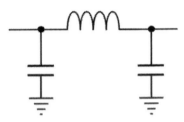

Figure E7C-2. Pi-network filter

QUESTION: How are the capacitors and inductors of a low-pass filter Pi-network arranged between the network's input and output? (E7C01)

ANSWER: **A capacitor is connected between the input and ground, another capacitor is connected between the output and ground, and an inductor is connected between input and output**

Pi networks can also be used to match the output impedance of one circuit to the input impedance of another or the output impedance of a transmitter to the input impedance of an antenna. An impedance-matching circuit transforms a complex impedance to a resistive impedance because it cancels the reactive part of the impedance and changes the resistive part to a desired value. One advantage of a Pi matching network over an L matching network consisting of a single inductor and a single capacitor is that the Q of Pi networks can be controlled by changing the value of the components.

QUESTION: How does an impedance-matching circuit transform a complex impedance to a resistive impedance? (E7C04)

ANSWER: **It cancels the reactive part of the impedance and changes the resistive part to a desired value**

QUESTION: What is one advantage of a Pi-matching network over an L-matching network consisting of a single inductor and a single capacitor? (E7C12)

ANSWER: **The Q of Pi-networks can be controlled**

A Pi network with an additional series inductor on the output is called a Pi-L network. They are often used for matching a vacuum-tube final amplifier to a 50-ohm unbalanced output. One advantage a Pi-L-network has over a Pi-network for impedance matching between the final amplifier of a vacuum-tube transmitter and an antenna is that it has greater harmonic suppression.

QUESTION: Which describes a Pi-L-network used for matching a vacuum tube final amplifier to a 50-ohm unbalanced output? (E7C07)

ANSWER: **A Pi-network with an additional series inductor on the output**

QUESTION: What advantage does a series-L Pi-L-network have over a series-L Pi-network for impedance matching between the final amplifier of a vacuum-tube transmitter and an antenna? (E7C03)

ANSWER: **Greater harmonic suppression**

In addition to being used to control the frequency of oscillators, piezoelectric crystals are used to build filters. A crystal lattice filter is a filter with narrow bandwidth and steep skirts made using quartz crystals. The relative frequencies of the individual crystals is the factor that has the greatest effect in helping determine the bandwidth and response shape of a crystal ladder filter. The narrowness of the bandwidth and the steepness of the skirts are sometimes called the filter's shape factor. The shape factor affects a filter's ability to reject signals on adjacent frequencies.

QUESTION: What is a crystal lattice filter? (E7C09)

ANSWER: **A filter with narrow bandwidth and steep skirts made using quartz crystals**

QUESTION: Which of the following factors has the greatest effect on the bandwidth and response shape of a crystal ladder filter? (E7C08)

ANSWER: **The relative frequencies of the individual crystals**

QUESTION: Which of the following describes a receiving filter's ability to reject signals occupying an adjacent channel? (E7C11)

ANSWER: **Shape factor**

Different types of filters have different characteristics. For example, a Chebyshev filter that has a sharp cutoff, but also ripple in the passband. An elliptical filter, on the other hand, has an extremely sharp cutoff with one or more notches in the stop band.

QUESTION: Which filter type is described as having ripple in the passband and a sharp cutoff? (E7C05)

ANSWER: **A Chebyshev filter**

QUESTION: What are the distinguishing features of an elliptical filter? (E7C06)

ANSWER: **Extremely sharp cutoff with one or more notches in the stop band**

Often, you'll choose a filter type for a particular application. For example, a cavity filter would be the best choice for use in a 2 meter repeater duplexer.

QUESTION: Which of the following filters would be the best choice for use in a 2 meter band repeater duplexer? (E7C10)

ANSWER: **A cavity filter**

E7D – Power supplies and voltage regulators; Solar array charge controllers

Linear power supplies are a type of power supply used in amateur radio stations. They are called linear power supplies because they use ICs called linear electronic voltage regulator to maintain a constant output voltage. The way they regulate the output voltage is to vary the conduction of current through a control element, usually a transistor. The circuit shown in Figure E7-2 below is a linear voltage regulator, and the control element is Q1. Q1, often called the pass transistor, controls the current supplied to the load, thereby keeping the output voltage constant even when the load varies. C2 bypasses rectifier output ripple around D1.

Figure E7-2

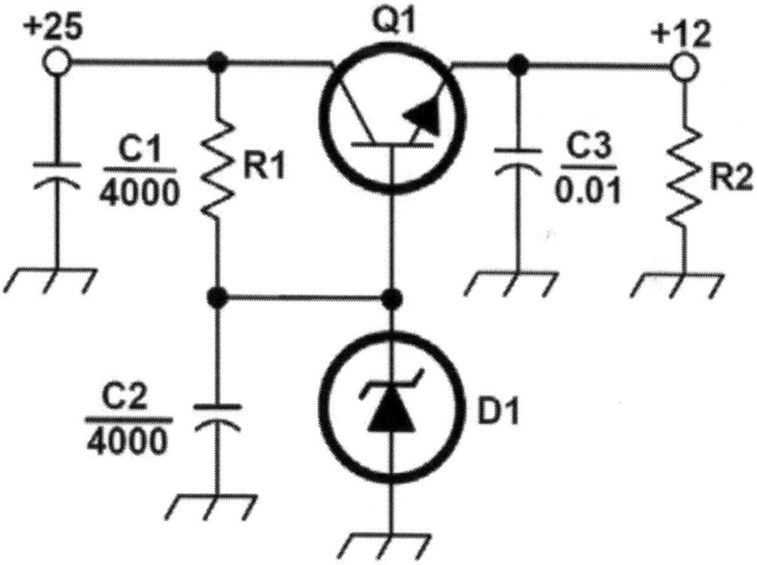

QUESTION: What type of circuit is shown in Figure E7-2? (E7D08)

ANSWER: **Linear voltage regulator**

QUESTION: How does a linear electronic voltage regulator work? (E7D01)

ANSWER: **The conduction of a control element is varied to maintain a constant output voltage**

QUESTION: What is the purpose of Q1 in the circuit shown in Figure E7-2? (E7D06)

ANSWER: **It controls the current supplied to the load**

QUESTION: What is the function of the pass transistor in a linear voltage regulator circuit? (E7D11)

ANSWER: **Maintains nearly constant output voltage over a wide range of load current**

QUESTION: What is the purpose of C2 in the circuit shown in Figure E7-2? (E7D07)

ANSWER: **It bypasses rectifier output ripple around D1**

Power supply designers typically use Zener diode as the voltage reference in a linear voltage regulator. D1 in Figure E7-2 is a zener diode.

QUESTION: What device is typically used as a stable voltage reference in a linear voltage regulator? (E7D03)

ANSWER: **A Zener diode**

There are two kinds of linear voltage regulators—the series regulator and the shunt regulator. A series regulator is the type of linear voltage regulator that usually makes the most efficient use of the primary power source. A shunt regulator is the type of linear voltage regulator that places a constant load on the unregulated voltage source.

QUESTION: Which of the following types of linear voltage regulator usually make the most efficient use of the primary power source? (E7D04)

ANSWER: **A series regulator**

QUESTION: Which of the following types of linear voltage regulator places a constant load on the unregulated voltage source? (E7D05)

ANSWER: **A shunt regulator**

An important analog voltage regulator specification is the drop-out voltage, which is the minimum input-to-output voltage required to maintain regulation. For example, if an analog voltage regulator has a drop-out voltage of 2 V, the input voltage must be at least 11 V in order to maintain an output voltage of 9 V.

QUESTION: What is the dropout voltage of an analog voltage regulator? (E7D12)

ANSWER: **Minimum input-to-output voltage required to maintain regulation**

Power dissipation is also important when designing a power supply with a series-connected linear voltage regulator. Excessive power dissipation reduces the efficiency of the supply and could require that you use large heat sinks to dissipate the power. The power dissipation by a series connected linear voltage regulator is the voltage difference from input to output multiplied by output current.

QUESTION: What is the equation for calculating power dissipated by a series linear voltage regulator? (E7D13)

ANSWER: **Voltage difference from input to output multiplied by output current**

Switching power supplies

Nowadays, you are as likely to find a switching power supply in an amateur radio station as you are a linear power supply. Switching power supplies use a much different method of regulating the output voltage than a linear supply. Instead of controlling the current through a control element, a switching supply varies the duty cycle of the control element to produce a constant average output voltage.

QUESTION: What is a characteristic of a switching electronic voltage regulator? (E7D02)

ANSWER: **The controlled device's duty cycle is changed to produce a constant average output voltage**

Switching power supplies are usually less expensive and lighter than a linear power supply with the same output rating. Switching supplies are also generally more efficient than linear power supplies. The main reason that a high-frequency switching type high voltage power supply can be less expensive, lighter in weight, and more efficient than a linear power supply is that the high frequency inverter design uses much smaller transformers and filter components for an equivalent power output. But, this comes at a cost. Switching supply circuits are more complicated than the circuitry in a linear supply and may generate RF noise.

QUESTION: What is the primary reason that a high-frequency switching type high-voltage power supply can be both less expensive and lighter in weight than a conventional power supply? (E7D10)

ANSWER: **The high frequency inverter design uses much smaller transformers and filter components for an equivalent power output**

High-voltage power supplies

Most HF transceivers and VHF/UHF transceivers operate at a relatively low voltage. This is normally around 12 – 15 VDC. Some devices, such as older tube equipment and linear amplifiers need higher voltages to operate. These power supplies are quite different than the low-voltage linear and switching supplies describe above.

High-voltage supplies may also have a step-start circuit. The purpose of a "step-start" circuit in a high-voltage power supply is to allow the filter capacitors to charge gradually, thereby reducing the amount of current the supply draws when turned on.

QUESTION: What is the purpose of a step-start circuit in a high-voltage power supply? (E7D15)

ANSWER: **To allow the filter capacitors to charge gradually**

When several electrolytic filter capacitors are connected in series to increase the operating voltage of a power supply filter circuit, resistors should be connected across each capacitor. Doing this helps to equalize the voltage drop across each capacitor, discharge the capacitors when the supply is turned off, and provide a minimum load on the supply.

QUESTION: What is the purpose of connecting equal-value resistors across power supply filter capacitors connected in series? (E7D14)

ANSWER: **All these choices are correct**

- Equalize the voltage across each capacitor

- Discharge the capacitors when voltage is removed

- Provide a minimum load on the supply

Solar array charge controllers

Solar array charge controllers are voltage or current regulators that are used when charging batteries from a solar array. The main reason to use a charge controller with a solar power system is to prevent battery damage by overcharging them. Most solar panels that are rated at 12 V actually output 16 to 20 V, and if that output is not regulated, batteries connected to the solar panel may be damaged from overcharging.

QUESTION: What is the main reason to use a charge controller with a solar power system? (E7D09)

ANSWER: **Prevention of battery damage due to overcharge**

E7E – Modulation and demodulation: reactance, phase and balanced modulators; detectors; mixer stages

Modulation is the process of adding information, such as voice or digital information, to a carrier signal. The most common types of modulation that we use in amateur radio are amplitude modulation (AM) and frequency modulation (FM). Single-sideband, or SSB, is a form of amplitude modulation.

To frequency modulate a carrier, a transmitter will sometimes use a modulator that varies the phase of the signal. This process is called phase modulation (PM), and the type of modulator used to phase modulate a signal is called a reactance modulator. It uses an electrically variable inductance or capacitance to produce PM or FM signals.

QUESTION: Which of the following can be used to generate FM phone emissions? (E7E01)

ANSWER: **A reactance modulator on the oscillator**

QUESTION: What is the function of a reactance modulator? (E7E02)

ANSWER: **To produce PM or FM signals by using an electrically variable inductance or capacitance**

When generating FM signals, a pre-emphasis network is often added to an FM transmitter to boost the higher audio frequencies. Conversely, de-emphasis is commonly used in FM communications receivers to maintain compatibility with transmitters using phase modulation.

QUESTION: What circuit is added to an FM transmitter to boost the higher audio frequencies? (E7E05)

ANSWER: **A pre-emphasis network**

QUESTION: Why is de-emphasis commonly used in FM communications receivers? (E7E06)

ANSWER: **For compatibility with transmitters using phase modulation**

Amplitude modulation and single-sideband signals are produced using mixer circuits. The carrier frequency and the baseband signals are input to the mixer circuit which produces an amplitude modulated output. In other words, the term baseband refers to the frequency range of a modulating signal prior to it being mixed with a carrier signal. A mixer combines the carrier and baseband signals and produces four different output frequencies: the two input frequencies and the sum and difference of the two input frequencies. When using a mixer, you must take care not to use too high of a signal level at the mixer inputs, or it may generate spurious products.

QUESTION: What is meant by the term "baseband" in radio communications? (E7E07)

ANSWER: **The frequency range occupied by a message signal prior to modulation**

QUESTION: What are the principal frequencies that appear at the output of a mixer circuit? (E7E08)

ANSWER: **The two input frequencies along with their sum and difference frequencies**

QUESTION: What occurs when an excessive amount of signal energy reaches a mixer circuit? (E7E09)

ANSWER: **Spurious mixer products are generated**

Single sideband is most often used for phone transmission on the HF bands and for weak-signal operation on the VHF and UHF bands. One way a single-sideband phone signal can be generated is by using a balanced modulator followed by a filter. A balanced modulator is a type of mixer, but its output contains only the two sidebands, not the carrier or baseband signal. A filter follows the balanced modulator to eliminate the undesired sideband.

QUESTION: What is one way a single-sideband phone signal can be generated? (E7E04)

ANSWER: **By using a balanced modulator followed by a filter**

At the receiving station, a modulated signal has to be demodulated.

Amplitude modulated signals are often demodulated using a simple diode detector circuit. A diode detector rectifies and filters a modulated signal, thereby producing an audio signal at its output. For demodulating SSB signals, you want something a little more sophisticated, like a product detector. A product detector is actually a frequency mixer, followed by a filter . Its output is the product of the modulated signal and a beat frequency oscillator, hence the name.

QUESTION: How does a diode envelope detector function? (E7E10)

ANSWER: **By rectification and filtering of RF signals**

QUESTION: Which type of detector circuit is used for demodulating SSB signals? (E7E11)

ANSWER: **Product detector**

FM receivers use a circuit called a discriminator to detect an FM signal. A discriminator converts a signal that changes in frequency to one that changes in amplitude.

QUESTION: What is a frequency discriminator stage in a FM receiver? (E7E03)

ANSWER: **A circuit for detecting FM signals**

E7F – DSP filtering and other operations; software defined radio fundamentals; DSP modulation and demodulation

Some modern radios modulate and demodulate signals entirely in software. This type of radio is called a software-defined radio, or SDR. One type of SDR uses a process called direct digital conversion to convert the analog radio signal into a series of numbers. What this type of SDR does is digitize an incoming RF signal with an analog-to-digital converter without being mixed with a local oscillator signal.

QUESTION: What is meant by direct digital conversion as applied to software defined radios? (E7F01)

ANSWER: **Incoming RF is digitized by an analog-to-digital converter without being mixed with a local oscillator signal**

Analog-to-digital converter specifications are crucial for a software-defined radio. Sample rate is one such specification. The sample rate determines the maximum receive bandwidth of a direct digital conversion SDR. An analog signal must be sampled at twice the rate of the highest frequency component of the signal by an analog-to-digital converter so that the signal can be accurately reproduced.

QUESTION: What aspect of receiver analog-to-digital conversion determines the maximum receive bandwidth of a Direct Digital Conversion SDR? (E7F10)

ANSWER: **Sample rate**

QUESTION: How frequently must an analog signal be sampled by an analog-to-digital converter so that the signal can be accurately reproduced? (E7F05)

ANSWER: **At least twice the rate of the highest frequency component of the signal**

Voltage resolution is also important. In the absence of atmospheric or thermal noise, the reference voltage level and sample width in bits sets the minimum detectable signal level for an SDR. The reference voltage is basically the maximum detectable voltage, while the number of bits determines the resolution of the analog-to-digital converter. For example, if an analog-to-digital converter had a reference voltage of 1 V, the minimum number of bits required to sample a signal at a resolution of 1 millivolt is 10 bits. The reason for this is that 2^{10} = 1,024, meaning that each bit represents approximately 1 mV.

QUESTION: What sets the minimum detectable signal level for a direct-sampling SDR receiver in the absence of atmospheric or thermal noise? (E7F11)

ANSWER: **Reference voltage level and sample width in bits**

QUESTION: What is the minimum number of bits required for an analog-to-digital converter to sample a signal with a range of 1 volt at a resolution of 1 millivolt? (E7F06)

ANSWER: **10 bits**

Modern software defined radios convert an incoming signal into two data streams: I and Q. The I and Q data streams are 90 degrees out of phase with one another, and as a result, the two data streams not only show how the amplitude of a signal is changing, but how the phase of a signal is changing. Perhaps the most common operation that is performed on the I and Q signals is a Fast Fourier Transform (FFT). The Fast Fourier Transform converts digital signals from the time domain to the frequency domain.

QUESTION: What function is performed by a Fast Fourier Transform? (E7F07)

ANSWER: **Converting digital signals from the time domain to the frequency domain**

Once a signal has been digitized, or converted into a series of numbers, it can be digitally filtered. We call this digital signal processing, or DSP For example, to remove unwanted noise from a received SSB signal you would use a DSP audio filter called an adaptive filter. Another type of digital filter used in SDRS is the finite impulse, or FIR, filter. An advantage of a Finite Impulse Response (FIR) filter vs an Infinite Impulse Response (IIR) digital filter is that FIR filters delay all frequency components of the signal by the same amount.

QUESTION: What kind of digital signal processing audio filter is used to remove unwanted noise from a received SSB signal? (E7F02)

ANSWER: **An adaptive filter**

QUESTION: Which of the following is an advantage of a Finite Impulse Response (FIR) filter vs an Infinite Impulse Response (IIR) digital filter? (E7F12)

ANSWER: **FIR filters can delay all frequency components of the signal by the same amount**

Taps in a digital signal processing filter provide incremental signal delays for filter algorithms. More taps would allow a digital signal processing filter to create a sharper filter response.

QUESTION: What is the function of taps in a digital signal processing filter? (E7F13)

ANSWER: **Provide incremental signal delays for filter algorithms**

QUESTION: Which of the following would allow a digital signal processing filter to create a sharper filter response? (E7F14)

ANSWER: **More taps**

Because so many calculations are required to do digital signal processing, SDRs sometimes use a technique called decimation, which allows them to use less-powerful processors. Decimation reduces the effective sample rate by removing samples when using a digital filter. They can get away with this because the signal of interest will usually have a significantly lower bandwidth than the digitized signal. An anti-aliasing digital filter must be used with a digital decimator because it peaks the response of the decimator, improving bandwidth.

QUESTION: What is the function of decimation? (E7F08)

ANSWER: **Reducing the effective sample rate by removing samples**

QUESTION: Why is an anti-aliasing digital filter required in a digital decimator? (E7F09)

ANSWER: **It removes high-frequency signal components that would otherwise be reproduced as lower frequency components**

Signals can also be generated using SDR techniques. For example, a common method of generating an SSB signal using digital signal processing is to combine signals with a quadrature phase relationship. The type of digital signal processing filter used to generate an SSB signal is a Hilbert-transform filter.

QUESTION: What is a common method of generating an SSB signal using digital signal processing? (E7F04)

ANSWER: **Signals are combined in quadrature phase relationship**

QUESTION: What type of digital signal processing filter is used to generate an SSB signal? (E7F03)

ANSWER: **A Hilbert-transform filter**

E7G – Active filters and op-amps: active audio filters; characteristics; basic circuit design; operational amplifiers

Operational amplifiers, or op-amps for short, are integrated circuits that include a high-gain, direct-coupled differential amplifier with very high input and very low output impedance. They can be used to build amplifiers, filter circuits, and many other types of circuits that do analog signal processing.

QUESTION: What is an operational amplifier? (E7G12)

ANSWER: **A high-gain, direct-coupled differential amplifier with very high input impedance and very low output impedance**

QUESTION: What is the typical input impedance of an op-amp? (E7G03)

ANSWER: **Very high**

QUESTION: What is the typical output impedance of an op-amp? (E7G01)

ANSWER: **Very low**

While the gain of an ideal operational amplifier does not vary with frequency, op amps in the real world do have a finite bandwidth. Some modern op amps can be used at high frequencies, but many of the older ones can't be used at frequencies above a couple of MHz. To find out if you can use an op amp at the frequency of your signals, check out the gain-bandwidth specification. The gain-bandwidth specification is the frequency at which the open-loop gain of the amplifier equals one.

QUESTION: How does the gain of an ideal operational amplifier vary with frequency? (E7G08)

ANSWER: **It does not vary with frequency**

QUESTION: What is the gain-bandwidth of an operational amplifier? (E7G06)

ANSWER: **The frequency at which the open-loop gain of the amplifier equals one**

Ideally, with no input signal, there should be no voltage difference between the two input terminals, and the output voltage should also be zero. Since no electronic component is ideal, there will be a voltage between these two terminals. We call this the input offset voltage. Put another way, the op-amp input-offset voltage is the differential input voltage needed to bring the open-loop output voltage to zero.

QUESTION: What is meant by the "op-amp input offset voltage"? (E7G04)

ANSWER: **The differential input voltage needed to bring the open loop output voltage to zero**

Because they are active components—that is to say that they amplify—filters made with op amps are called active filters. One use for an op-amp active filter is as an audio filter in a receiver. The values of capacitors and resistors external to the op-amp primarily determine the gain and frequency characteristics of an op-amp RC active filter.

Ringing is one undesirable characteristic of an op-amp filter. One effect of ringing in a filter is that it adds undesired oscillations to the desired signal. One way to prevent unwanted ringing and audio instability in a multi-section op-amp RC audio filter circuit is to restrict both gain and Q.

QUESTION: What is ringing in a filter? (E7G02)

ANSWER: **Undesired oscillations added to the desired signal**

QUESTION: How can unwanted ringing and audio instability be prevented in an op-amp RC audio filter circuit? (E7G05)

ANSWER: **Restrict both gain and Q**

Calculating the gain and output voltage of an op amp circuit is relatively straightforward. The gain is simply R_F/R_{in}. In the op amp circuit shown in

Figure E7-3, $R_{in} = R_1$. The output voltage of a circuit is then the input voltage times the gain.

Figure E7-3

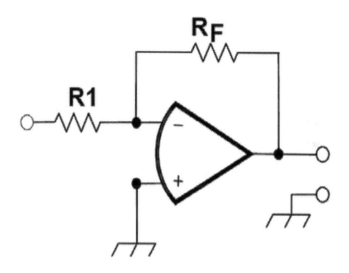

QUESTION: What magnitude of voltage gain can be expected from the circuit in Figure E73 when R1 is 10 ohms and RF is 470 ohms? (E7G07)

ANSWER: **47**

If R1 is 10 ohms and RF is 470 ohms, the gain is 470/10, or 47.

QUESTION: What absolute voltage gain can be expected from the circuit in Figure E7-3 when R1 is 1800 ohms and RF is 68 kilohms? (E7G10)

ANSWER: **38**

If R1 is 1800 ohms and RF is 68 kilohms, the gain is 68,000/1,800, or about 38.

QUESTION: What absolute voltage gain can be expected from the circuit in Figure E7-3 when R1 is 3300 ohms and RF is 47 kilohms? (E7G11)

ANSWER: **14**

If R1 is 3300 ohms and RF is 47 kilohms, the gain is 47,000/3,300, or about 14.

QUESTION: What will be the output voltage of the circuit shown in Figure E7-3 if R1 is 1000 ohms, RF is 10,000 ohms, and 0.23 volts DC is applied to the input? (E7G09)

ANSWER: **-2.3 volts**

If R1 is 1000 ohms, R$_F$ is 10,000 ohms, the gain of the circuit will be 10,000/1,000 or 10, and the output voltage will be equal to the input voltage times the gain. 0.23 V × 10 = 2.3 V, but since the input voltage is being applied to the negative input, the output voltage will be negative.

E7H – Oscillators and signal sources: types of oscillators; synthesizers and phase-locked loops; direct digital synthesizers; stabilizing thermal drift; microphonics; high-accuracy oscillators

Oscillator circuits are one of the basic building blocks of amateur radio equipment. Oscillator circuits are not only used to generate the signals we transmit, they are also an integral part of receivers, such as the superheterodyne receiver.

You can think of an oscillator as an amplifier with a tuned circuit that provides positive feedback. This tuned circuit might be an LC circuit or a crystal. The values of the components in the tuned circuit determine the output frequency of the oscillator. There are three types of oscillator circuits commonly used in Amateur Radio equipment: Colpitts, Hartley and Pierce. Colpitts and Hartley oscillator circuits are commonly used in VFOs.

QUESTION: What are three oscillator circuits used in amateur radio equipment? (E7H01)

ANSWER: **Colpitts, Hartley and Pierce**

QUESTION: Which of the following oscillator circuits are commonly used in VFOs? (E7H06)

ANSWER: **Colpitts and Hartley**

In a Hartley oscillator (shown in the figure below), positive feedback is supplied through a tapped coil.

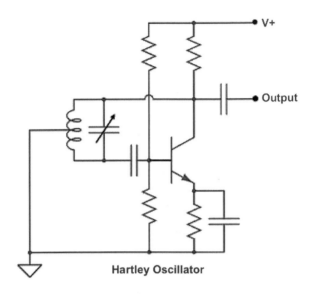

Hartley Oscillator

QUESTION: How is positive feedback supplied in a Hartley oscillator? (E7H03)

ANSWER: **Through a tapped coil**

In a Colpitts oscillator (shown below), positive feedback is supplied through a capacitive divider.

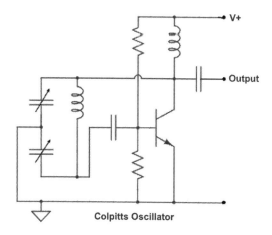

Colpitts Oscillator

QUESTION: How is positive feedback supplied in a Colpitts oscillator? (E7H04)

ANSWER: **Through a capacitive divider**

In a Pierce oscillator (shown below), positive feedback is supplied through a quartz crystal. To ensure that a crystal oscillator provides the frequency specified by the crystal manufacturer, you must provide the crystal with a specified parallel capacitance.

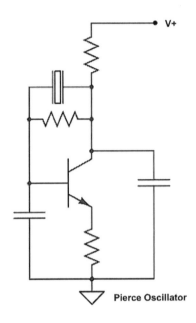

Pierce Oscillator

QUESTION: How is positive feedback supplied in a Pierce oscillator? (E7H05)

ANSWER: **Through a quartz crystal**

QUESTION: Which of the following must be done to ensure that a crystal oscillator provides the frequency specified by the crystal manufacturer? (E7H12)

ANSWER: **Provide the crystal with a specified parallel capacitance**

One problem that can occur with oscillators that use LC circuits is that their output frequency drifts because as the capacitors heat up their values change and the resonant frequency of the LC circuit changes. This phenomenon is called thermal drift. To prevent this from happening, use NPO capacitors. The capacitance of NPO capacitors changes very little over normal operating temperatures.

QUESTION: Which of the following components can be used to reduce thermal drift in crystal oscillators? (E7H08)

ANSWER: **NP0 capacitors**

Another problem that oscillators sometimes have is called microphonics. We say that an oscillator has a microphonic problem if the oscillator frequency changes due to mechanical vibration. An oscillator's microphonic responses can be reduced by mechanically isolating the oscillator from its enclosure.

QUESTION: What is a microphonic? (E7H02)

ANSWER: **Changes in oscillator frequency due to mechanical vibration**

QUESTION: How can an oscillator's microphonic responses be reduced? (E7H07)

ANSWER: **Mechanically isolate the oscillator circuitry from its enclosure**

Digital frequency synthesizers

Most modern amateur radio transceivers use digital frequency synthesizers instead of analog oscillators to generate RF signals. One reason for this is that they are much more stable than analog oscillators. The two main types of digital frequency synthesizers are the direct digital synthesizer and the phase-locked loop synthesizer.

A direct digital synthesizer is the type of frequency synthesizer circuit that uses a phase accumulator, lookup table, digital to analog converter and a low-pass anti-alias filter. The information contained in the lookup table of a direct digital frequency synthesizer are the amplitude values that represent a sine-wave output.

QUESTION: What type of frequency synthesizer circuit uses a phase accumulator, lookup table, digital to analog converter, and a low-pass anti-alias filter? (E7H09)

ANSWER: **A direct digital synthesizer**

QUESTION: What information is contained in the lookup table of a direct digital synthesizer (DDS)? (E7H10)

ANSWER: **Amplitude values that represent the desired waveform**

Frequency synthesizers that use phase-locked loops are also popular. A phase-locked loop is an electronic servo loop consisting of a phase detector, a low-pass filter, a voltage-controlled oscillator, and a stable reference oscillator. Frequency synthesis, FM demodulation are two functions that can be performed by a phase-locked loop.

QUESTION: What is a phase-locked loop circuit? (E7H14)

ANSWER: **An electronic servo loop consisting of a phase detector, a low-pass filter, a voltage-controlled oscillator, and a stable reference oscillator**

QUESTION: Which of these functions can be performed by a phase-locked loop? (E7H15)

ANSWER: **Frequency synthesis, FM demodulation**

Both direct digital synthesizers and phase-locked loop synthesizers have issues with spectral purity. The major spectral impurity components of direct digital synthesizers are spurious signals at discrete frequencies.

QUESTION: What are the major spectral impurity components of direct digital synthesizers? (E7H11)

ANSWER: **Spurious signals at discrete frequencies**

Because frequency multipliers are often used for generating RF signals at microwave frequencies, it is very important that the oscillators used in microwave transmitters are highly accurate and stable. Any inaccuracy or instability will be multiplied along with the desired frequency. To achieve high accurate and stability, oscillators used for microwave transmission and reception, can use a GPS signal reference, a rubidium stabilized reference oscillator, or a temperature-controlled high Q dielectric resonator.

QUESTION: Which of the following is a technique for providing highly accurate and stable oscillators needed for microwave transmission and reception? (E7H13)

ANSWER: **All these choices are correct**

- Use a GPS signal reference

- Use a rubidium stabilized reference oscillator

- Use a temperature-controlled high Q dielectric resonator

E8: SIGNALS AND EMISSIONS

E8A – AC waveforms: sine, square, and irregular waveforms; AC measurements; average power and PEP of RF signals; Fourier analysis; analog to digital conversion: digital to analog conversion; advantages of digital communications

We use all different kinds of waveforms in amateur radio. It is, therefore, important to know about the different types of waveforms and how to measure their parameters. One parameter of an AC waveform that you need to know is its root mean square, or RMS, value. The root-mean-square value of an AC voltage is the DC voltage causing the same amount of heating in a resistor as the corresponding RMS AC voltage. If the waveform is regular, it's relatively easy to calculate the RMS value. In the case of a sine wave, the RMS value is 0.707 times the peak value. You use the RMS voltage value to calculate the power of a wave.

If the waveform is a complex waveform, however, to determine its RMS value, you must take a number of measurements over a period of time and then calculate the RMS value. That's what true RMS meters do. That's why they make more accurate RMS voltage measurements than meters that aren't true-RMS meters.

> QUESTION: What of the following instruments would be the most accurate for measuring the RMS voltage of a complex waveform? (E8A05)
>
> ANSWER: **A true-RMS calculating meter**

To calculate the average power of an AC or RF signal, knowing the RMS voltage is important. You use the RMS voltage to calculate the average power.

Another important parameter of an RF signal is the peak envelope power (PEP). PEP is the highest instantaneous value achieved by the signal. Consider single sideband signals, for example. Because a single sideband signal is amplitude modulated by the operator's voice, the operator's speech characteristics determine both the average power and instantaneous power. The higher the instantaneous audio level, the higher the instantaneous power, and the higher the average audio level, the higher the average output power.

QUESTION: What determines the PEP-to-average power ratio of a single-sideband phone signal? E8A07)

ANSWER: **Speech characteristics**

If you know the peak envelope power (PEP), though, you can make a pretty good guess at the average power. The approximate ratio of PEP-to-average power in a typical single-sideband phone signal is 2.5 to 1. Put another way, the average power of an SSB signal is about 40% of the peak power.

QUESTION: What is the approximate ratio of PEP-to-average power in a typical single-sideband phone signal? (E8A06)

ANSWER: **2.5 to 1**

To make use of digital techniques in amateur radio, such as digital signal processing or DSP, we must convert analog signals to digital signals and vice-versa. To do this, we use an analog-to-digital converter (ADC). An ADC converts the instantaneous value of an input signal to a numerical value. The number of output bits determine the resolution of the converter. An analog-to-digital converter with 8 bit resolution can encode 256 levels.

QUESTION: How many different input levels can be encoded by an analog-to-digital converter with 8-bit resolution? (E8A09)

ANSWER: **256**

Software-defined radios use ADCs to digitize incoming signals almost as soon as the signal enters the radio. The analog-to-digital converters must therefore accurately convert the analog signal to a series of numbers. One measure of the quality of an analog-to-digital converter is total harmonic distortion, or THD. THD is a measure of how the harmonics of a signal distort the signal and is the ratio of the sum of the powers of all harmonic components to the power of the fundamental frequency.

QUESTION: Which of the following is a measure of the quality of an analog-to-digital converter? (E8A11)

ANSWER: **Total harmonic distortion**

To convert radio signals to digital streams used in software-defined radios, you need to sample the signal at a very high rate in order to preserve signal integrity. Because they allow digitizing signals at very high frequencies, many SDRs use ADCs that use a technique called flash conversion.

QUESTION: Why would a direct or flash conversion analog-to-digital converter be useful for a software defined radio? (E8A08)

ANSWER: Very high speed allows digitizing high frequencies

Successive approximation is another analog-to-digital conversion technique. A successive approximation ADC continually compares the input voltage to a voltage generated by the successive approximation register and a digital-to-analog converter. This voltage is increased or decreased depending on whether this reference voltage is greater than or less than the input voltage. This process continues until the input voltage matches the reference voltage. Successive approximation ADCs are not as fast as flash converters, but they're very accurate and cost less than flash converters.

QUESTION: Which of the following is a type of analog-to-digital conversion? (E8A02)

ANSWER: **Successive approximation**

One technique sometimes used when performing analog-to-digital conversion is called dithering. Circuits that use dithering add a small amount of noise to improve the accuracy of an analog-to-digital converter.

QUESTION: What is "dither" with respect to analog-to-digital converters? (E8A04)

ANSWER: **A small amount of noise added to the input signal to allow more precise representation of a signal over time**

SDRs also use digital-to-analog converters (DACs). Sometimes signals are passed through a low pass filter after being output from a DAC to remove harmonics from the output. This produces a cleaner output signal.

QUESTION: What is the purpose of a low-pass filter used in conjunction with a digital-to-analog converter? (E8A10)

ANSWER: **Remove harmonics from the output caused by the discrete analog levels generated**

SDR software makes a lot of use of the Fourier transform. By performing Fourier analysis on an incoming data stream, the SDR radio is able to determine the frequency content of a signal and then using that information, perform different digital signal processing operations on the signal. For example, by using Fourier analysis, you can show that the frequency content of a square wave contains its fundamental frequency and all of its odd harmonics. A Fourier analysis of a sawtooth wave shows that its frequency content includes the fundamental frequency plus all of its harmonics.

QUESTION: What is the name of the process that shows that a square wave is made up of a sine wave plus all its odd harmonics? (E8A01)

ANSWER: **Fourier analysis**

QUESTION: What type of wave does a Fourier analysis show to be made up of sine waves of a given fundamental frequency plus all its harmonics? (E8A03)

ANSWER: **A sawtooth wave**

E8B – Modulation and demodulation: modulation methods; modulation index and deviation ratio; frequency and time division multiplexing; Orthogonal Frequency Division Multiplexing

In FM modulation, the two primary parameters of interest are deviation ratio and modulation index. Deviation ratio is the ratio of the maximum deviation to the highest audio modulating frequency. For example, the deviation ratio of an FM-phone signal having a maximum deviation of ± 5 kHz when the maximum modulation frequency is 3 kHz is 5 kHz/3 kHz, or 1.67.

QUESTION: What is deviation ratio? (E8B09)

ANSWER: **The ratio of the maximum carrier frequency deviation to the highest audio modulating frequency**

QUESTION: What is the deviation ratio of an FM-phone signal having a maximum frequency swing of plus-or-minus 5 kHz when the maximum modulation frequency is 3 kHz? (E8B05)

ANSWER: **1.67**

QUESTION: What is the deviation ratio of an FM-phone signal having a maximum frequency swing of plus or minus 7.5 kHz when the maximum modulation frequency is 3.5 kHz? (E8B06)

ANSWER: **2.14**

The modulation index is the ratio between the frequency deviation of an FM phone signal and the modulating signal frequency. For example, the modulation index of an FM-phone signal having a maximum frequency deviation of 3000 Hz either side of the carrier frequency, when the modulating frequency is 1000 Hz is 3000 Hz/ 1000 Hz, or 3. Note that the modulation index of frequency-modulated and phase-modulated emissions does not depend on the RF carrier frequency.

QUESTION: What is the modulation index of an FM signal?

(E8B01)

ANSWER: **The ratio of frequency deviation to modulating signal frequency**

QUESTION: How does the modulation index of a phase-modulated emission vary with RF carrier frequency? (E8B02)

ANSWER: **It does not depend on the RF carrier frequency**

QUESTION: What is the modulation index of an FM-phone signal having a maximum frequency deviation of 3000 Hz either side of the carrier frequency when the modulating frequency is 1000 Hz? (E8B03)

ANSWER: **3**

QUESTION: What is the modulation index of an FM-phone signal having a maximum carrier deviation of plus or minus 6 kHz when modulated with a 2 kHz modulating frequency? (E8B04)

ANSWER: **3**

Some communications systems use multiplexing techniques to combine several separate analog information streams into a single analog radio frequency signal. Systems that use frequency division multiplexing, merge two or more information streams into a "baseband," which then modulates the transmitter. Systems that use digital time division multiplexing, arrange two or more signals to share discrete time slots of a data transmission.

QUESTION: What is frequency division multiplexing? (E8B10)

ANSWER: **Two or more information streams are merged into a baseband, which then modulates the transmitter**

QUESTION: What is digital time division multiplexing? (E8B11)

ANSWER: **Two or more signals are arranged to share**

discrete time slots of a data transmission

Orthogonal Frequency Division Multiplexing (OFDM) is a type of frequency multiplexing used for high speed digital modes. OFDM uses subcarriers at frequencies chosen to avoid intersymbol interference.

QUESTION: Orthogonal Frequency Division Multiplexing is a technique used for which type of amateur communication? (E8B07)

ANSWER: **High-speed digital modes**

QUESTION: What describes Orthogonal Frequency Division Multiplexing? (E8B08)

ANSWER: **A digital modulation technique using subcarriers at frequencies chosen to avoid intersymbol interference**

E8C – Digital signals: digital communications modes; information rate vs. bandwidth; error correction

Digital modes have become very popular in amateur radio lately, but Morse Code, the type of modulation that has been around the longest, is the original digital mode. One advantage of using Morse Code is that it has a very narrow bandwidth. Several factors affect the bandwidth of a CW signal, including the keying speed and the shape factor (rise and fall time) of the signal. For example, the bandwidth necessary for a 13-wpm International Morse Code transmission is approximately 52 Hz, while the bandwidth of a 25-wpm transmission would be somewhat higher.

> QUESTION: What is the approximate bandwidth of a 13-WPM International Morse Code transmission? (E8C05)
>
> ANSWER: **52 Hz**
>
> QUESTION: What factors affect the bandwidth of a transmitted CW signal? (E8C12)
>
> ANSWER: **Keying speed and shape factor (rise and fall time)**

The bandwidth needed for frequency-shift keying (FSK) digital transmissions similarly increases as the data rate increases. The formula for calculating the bandwidth, given the baud rate and frequency shift is:

BW (Hz) = frequency shift × 1.2 + baud rate

Using this equation, we see that the bandwidth necessary for a 170-hertz shift, 300-baud ASCII transmission is 170 Hz × 1.2 + 300 = 204 +300, or about 0.5 kHz. Similarly, the bandwidth of a 4800-Hz frequency shift, 9600-baud ASCII FM transmission is 4800 × 1.2 + 9600 = 5760 +9600 = 15.36 kHz.

> QUESTION: What is the bandwidth of a 170-hertz shift, 300-baud ASCII transmission? (E8C06)
>
> ANSWER: **0.5 kHz**
>
> QUESTION: What is the bandwidth of a 4800-Hz frequency

shift, 9600-baud ASCII FM transmission? (E8C07)

ANSWER: **15.36 kHz**

One of the basic principles of digital communications is that signals with a higher data rate occupy a wider bandwidth. While this is true if both transmissions are using the same digital code, it is possible to sometimes increase the symbol rate of a digital transmission by using a more efficient code.

QUESTION: How may data rate be increased without increasing bandwidth? (E8C10)

ANSWER: **Using a more efficient digital code**

PSK31 has become a very popular digital mode. One reason for this is that it occupies a very narrow bandwidth—only 31 Hz. One technique used to minimize the bandwidth requirements of a PSK31 signal is the use of sinusoidal data pulses. Another way to minimize bandwidth when using phase shift keying is to shift phase at the zero crossing of the RF signal.

QUESTION: What technique minimizes the bandwidth of a PSK31 signal? (E8C04)

ANSWER: **Use of sinusoidal data pulses**

QUESTION: Why should phase-shifting of a PSK signal be done at the zero crossing of the RF signal? (E8C03)

ANSWER: **To minimize bandwidth**

When digital communication systems were first developed, data was sent one bit at a time. As the need for faster data transmission grew, engineers figured out how to send multiple bit simultaneously. Instead of sending single bits, these systems send and receive "symbols," which represent multiple bits. As a result, we often refer to the speed of a digital transmission as the symbol rate, not the bit rate. The symbol rate is the rate at which the waveform of a transmitted signal changes to convey information. Another term that you often hear is baud rate. Baud rate and symbol rate are the same thing.

QUESTION: What is the definition of symbol rate in a digital transmission? (E8C02)

ANSWER: **The rate at which the waveform changes to convey information**

QUESTION: What is the relationship between symbol rate and baud? (E8C11)

ANSWER: **They are the same**

Whenever digital data is sent over a radio channel, it is encoded. Gray codes are often used for this purpose. The reason for this is that Gray code allows only one bit to change between sequential code values. This feature facilitates error detection.

QUESTION: Which digital code allows only one bit to change between sequential code values? (E8C09)

ANSWER: **Gray code**

There are many things that can cause errors in a data stream. For example, an interfering signal might cause a receiver to interpret a transmitted symbol incorrectly. When these errors are not allowable, digital communications systems implement some form of error detection and correction.

One way to achieve reliable data communication is to use the Automatic Repeat ReQuest, or ARQ, protocol. Systems that use ARQ error control request a sender to retransmit packets if they detect errors. Senders will also re-transmit a data packet if they do not receive an acknowledgement from the receiver that it has correctly received a packet.

QUESTION: How does ARQ accomplish error correction? (E8C08)

ANSWER: **If errors are detected, a retransmission is requested**

Another way to correct errors is a technique called forward error correction. Systems that use forward error correction, such as the FreeDV digital voice mode, transmit extra data that receiving stations use to detect and correct errors. No retransmission is needed. The disadvantage, of course, is that more data than strictly necessary must be sent, and this slows down the overall data rate.

QUESTION: How is Forward Error Correction implemented? (E8C01)

ANSWER: **By transmitting extra data that may be used to detect and correct transmission errors**

E8D – Keying defects and overmodulation of digital signals; digital codes; spread spectrum

It is good amateur practice to ensure that the CW and digital signals you transmit are high quality. Perhaps the biggest problem that you'll have when sending CW signals is key clicks. Key clicks are spurious signals that your transmitter generates when the rise and fall times of your CW signal are extremely short. The most common method of reducing key clicks is, therefore, to increase keying waveform rise and fall times. Fortunately, most modern transceivers allow you to set the rise and fall times of the CW signal, so this is an easy fix.

> QUESTION: What is the primary effect of extremely short rise or fall time on a CW signal? (E8D04)
>
> ANSWER: **The generation of key clicks**
>
> QUESTION: What is the most common method of reducing key clicks? (E8D05)
>
> ANSWER: **Increase keying waveform rise and fall times**

To ensure high-quality digital signals, such as when transmitting audio frequency shift signals, such as PSK31, you need to set the audio input level properly. A common cause of overmodulation of AFSK signals is excessive transmit audio levels. To determine if you are using excessive input audio levels and over-modulating an AFSK signal to the point of distortion, you would measure the intermodulation distortion (IMD) of the signal. A good minimum IMD level for an idling PSK signal is -30 dB.

> QUESTION: What is a common cause of overmodulation of AFSK signals? (E8D07)
>
> ANSWER: **Excessive transmit audio levels**
>
> QUESTION: What parameter evaluates distortion of an AFSK signal caused by excessive input audio levels? (E8D08)
>
> ANSWER: **Intermodulation Distortion (IMD)**
>
> QUESTION: What is considered an acceptable maximum

IMD level for an idling PSK signal? (E8D09)

ANSWER: **-30 dB**

Digital codes

Although ASCII and Unicode have now become standard codes for sending textual information, we still use the Baudot code when sending and receiving RTTY. Some of the differences between the Baudot digital code and ASCII are:

- Baudot uses 5 data bits per character, ASCII uses 7 or 8.
- Baudot uses 2 characters as letters/figures shift codes, ASCII has no letters/figures shift code.

QUESTION: What are some of the differences between the Baudot digital code and ASCII? (E8D10)

ANSWER: **Baudot uses 5 data bits per character, ASCII uses 7 or 8; Baudot uses 2 characters as letters/figures shift codes, ASCII has no letters/figures shift code**

Even though it uses more bits per character, ASCII does have some advantages over Baudot. For example, one advantage of using ASCII code for data communications is that you can transmit both upper and lower case text.

QUESTION: What is one advantage of using ASCII code for data communications? (E8D11)

ANSWER: **It is possible to transmit both upper and lower case text**

In an eight-bit ASCII character, the eighth bit is the parity bit. The advantage of including a parity bit with an ASCII character stream is that some types of errors can be detected. In systems that use even parity, the parity bit is set to either a one or a zero, so that the number of ones in the character is equal to an even number. In systems that use odd parity, the parity bit is set to either a one or a zero, so that the number of ones in the character is equal to an odd number.

QUESTION: What is the advantage of including parity bits

in ASCII characters? (E8D06)

ANSWER: **Some types of errors can be detected**

Spread spectrum

Amateurs can now use spread-spectrum techniques on all bands above 420 MHz. The reason these bands are used is because spread-spectrum signals require more bandwidth than is available on the lower frequency bands.

Spread spectrum transmissions generally change frequency very rapidly according to a particular sequence also used by the receiving station during a transmission. This is called frequency hopping. A direct sequence, spread spectrum communications system uses a high-speed binary bit stream to shift the phase of an RF carrier.

QUESTION: How does the spread spectrum technique of frequency hopping work? (E8D03)

ANSWER: **The frequency of the transmitted signal is changed very rapidly according to a pseudorandom sequence also used by the receiving station**

QUESTION: What spread spectrum communications technique uses a high-speed binary bit stream to shift the phase of an RF carrier? (E8D02)

ANSWER: **Direct sequence**

Because transmission and reception occur over a wide band of frequencies, spread spectrum communications are more resistant to interference on a single frequency than are conventional communications systems. The reason for this is that signals not using the spread spectrum algorithm are suppressed in the receiver.

QUESTION: Why are received spread spectrum signals resistant to interference? (E8D01)

ANSWER: **Signals not using the spread spectrum algorithm are suppressed in the receiver**

E9: ANTENNAS AND TRANSMISSION LINES

E9A Basic antenna parameters: radiation resistance, gain, beamwidth, efficiency, effective radiated power

Antenna gain is one of the most misunderstood topics in amateur radio. There are several reasons for this, including:

- Antennas don't really have gain in the same way that an amplifier has gain. When you use a linear amplifier, you get more power out than you put in. Since transmitting antennas are passive devices, there's no way to get more power out than you put in.

- It's not easy to measure antenna gain. There is no antenna gain meter that you can simply hook up to an antenna to measure its gain.

So, what is meant by antenna gain? Antenna gain is the ratio of the radiated signal strength of an antenna in the direction of maximum radiation to that of a reference antenna. What this means is that when you talk about antenna gain, you have to know what kind of antenna you're comparing it to.

When talking about antenna gain, antenna engineers often refer to the "isotropic antenna." In practice, an isotropic antenna is a theoretical antenna that has no gain in any direction. That is to say it radiates the power input to it equally in all directions.

QUESTION: What is an isotropic antenna? (E9A01)

ANSWER: **A theoretical, omnidirectional antenna used as a reference for antenna gain**

Let's take a look at a practical example. The 1/2-wavelength dipole antenna is the most basic amateur radio antenna. The dipole actually has some gain over isotropic antenna. The reason for this is that it is directional. The signal strength transmitted broadside to the antenna will be greater than the signal strength transmitted off the ends of the antenna.

The gain of a 1/2-wavelength dipole in free space compared to an isotropic antenna is 2.15 dB. Sometimes, you'll see this value as 2.15 dBi, where dBi denotes that an isotropic antenna is being used for this comparison. Since the isotropic antenna is a theoretical antenna, some think it's better to compare an antenna to a dipole antenna. Let's look at an example:

> QUESTION: How much gain does an antenna have
> compared to a 1/2-wavelength dipole when it has 6 dB gain
> over an isotropic antenna? (E9A12)
>
> ANSWER: **3.85 dB**

You obtain this value by simply subtracting 2.15 dB from the 6 dB figure:

> Gain over a dipole = gain over an isotropic antenna - 2.15 dB =
> 6 dBi - 2.15 dBi = 3.85 dBd

Sometimes, the gain over a dipole is denoted as dBd.

Effective radiated power

When you use an antenna that has gain, you are increasing the effectiveness of the power input to it in the direction the antenna is pointing. We call this the effective radiated power, but it is not just the transmitter's output power times the gain of the antenna. You also have to take into account losses in other parts of the antenna system.

This is especially true for VHF and UHF repeater systems, where losses in the feedline, duplexer, and circulator can be significant. The power that reaches the antenna may be substantially lower than the power output of the transmitter.

Let's look at an example. Say that your repeater station had a transmitter output power of 150 watts, a feed line loss of 2 dB, 2.2 dB duplexer loss, and 7 dBd antenna gain. To calculate the effective radiated power, you have to first subtract the losses from the gain, as expressed in dB to get the total gain of the system:

> total system gain = 7 dB − 2 dB − 2.2 dB = 2.8 dB.

Now, recall that 3 dB corresponds to a power ratio of 2:1, as shown in the table below. 2.8 dB would then be slightly less than that. In fact, 2.8dB corresponds to a power ratio of approximately 1.905, so the effective radiated power is the transmitter output power times the total system gain:

effective radiated power = 150 W x 1.905 = 286 W.

dB	Gain	Loss
3	X2	X1/2
6	X4	X1/4
10	X10	X1/10

QUESTION: What term describes station output, taking into account all gains and losses? (E9A13)

ANSWER: **Effective radiated power**

QUESTION: What is the effective radiated power relative to a dipole of a repeater station with 150 watts transmitter power output, 2 dB feed line loss, 2.2 dB duplexer loss, and 7 dBd antenna gain? (E9A02)

ANSWER: **286 watts**

Let's look at another example. In this example, your repeater station has 200 watts transmitter power output, 4 dB feed line loss, 3.2 dB duplexer loss, 0.8 dB circulator loss, and 10 dBd antenna gain. The total gain of the system is, therefore, 10 dB – 4 dB – 3.2 dB – 0.8 dB, or 2.0 dB. 2.0 dB corresponds to a power ratio of approximately 1.585, making the effective radiated power 200 W × 1.585 = 317 W. Note that in this system, the high feedline and duplexer losses almost completely negate the benefit of using a high gain antenna.

QUESTION: What is the effective radiated power relative to a dipole of a repeater station with 200 watts transmitter power output, 4 dB feed line loss, 3.2 dB duplexer loss, 0.8 dB circulator loss, and 10 dBd antenna gain? (E9A06)

ANSWER: **317 watts**

Here's a third example. Notice that in this example we are comparing the effective radiated power to an isotropic antenna, not a dipole. In this example, the repeater station has 200 watts transmitter power output, 2 dB feed line loss, 2.8 dB duplexer loss, 1.2 dB circulator loss, and 7 dBi antenna gain. The total gain of the system is 7 dB – 2 dB – 2.8 dB – 1.2 dB, or 1.0 dB. 1.0 dB corresponds to a power ratio of approximately 1.26, and the effective radiated power equals 200 W × 1.26 = 252 W.

QUESTION: What is the effective isotropic radiated power of a repeater station with 200 watts transmitter power output, 2 dB feed line loss, 2.8 dB duplexer loss, 1.2 dB circulator loss, and 7 dBi antenna gain? (E9A07)

ANSWER: **252 watts**

Feedpoint impedance

Other antenna parameters are also important, of course. One of the most basic antenna parameters is the feedpoint impedance. The reason that the feedpoint impedance is important is that you want the feedpoint impedance to match the impedance of the feedline that you use and the output impedance of the transmitter. When these are all equal, we say that the system is "matched," and it will radiate the maximum amount of energy.

Many factors may affect the feed point impedance of an antenna, including antenna height, conductor length/diameter ratio and location of nearby conductive objects. For example, we say that the feedpoint impedance of a half-wavelength, dipole antenna is 72 Ω, but that's only really true if the antenna is in free space. When it's closer to the ground than a quarter wavelength, then the impedance will be different. That's why you have to tune the antenna when you install it.

QUESTION: Which of the following factors affect the feed point impedance of an antenna? (E9A04)

ANSWER: **Antenna height**

Radiation resistance

Another antenna parameter that's frequently bandied about is radiation resistance. The radiation resistance of an antenna is the value of a resistance that would dissipate the same amount of power as that radiated from an antenna. In the case of an antenna, however, that power isn't being turned into heat, but rather turned into radio waves. The total resistance of an antenna system is the sum of the radiation resistance and ohmic resistance. The ohmic resistance is the combination of all the physical resistances in the system, including the resistance of the antenna wire, feed line, and connections.

> QUESTION: What is the radiation resistance of an antenna? (E9A03)
>
> ANSWER: **The value of a resistance that would dissipate the same amount of power as that radiated from an antenna**

> QUESTION: What is included in the total resistance of an antenna system? (E9A05)
>
> ANSWER: **Radiation resistance plus loss resistance**

If you know the radiation resistance and the ohmic resistance of an antenna, you can calculate its efficiency. Antenna efficiency equals the radiation resistance divided by the total resistance.

> QUESTION: What is antenna efficiency? (E9A09)
>
> ANSWER: **Radiation resistance divided by total resistance**

Vertical antennas, bandwidth

Vertical antennas are sometimes criticized as being inefficient antennas. The main reason for this is the lack of a good radial system. Installing a good radial system will improve a quarter-wave vertical's efficiency. Another reason for poor vertical performance is poor soil conductivity. If soil conductivity is poor, ohmic resistance will be high, and the antenna's efficiency will be low.

> QUESTION: Which of the following improves the efficiency of a ground-mounted quarter-wave vertical antenna? (E9A10)

ANSWER: **Installing a radial system**

QUESTION: Which of the following factors determines ground losses for a ground-mounted vertical antenna operating in the 3 MHz to 30 MHz range? (E9A11)

ANSWER: **Soil conductivity**

When selecting an antenna, you have to consider the antenna's bandwidth. Antenna bandwidth is the frequency range over which an antenna satisfies a performance requirement. Normally, the performance requirement is an SWR of 2:1 or less. In fact, you'll sometimes hear this parameter referred to as the 2:1 SWR bandwidth.

QUESTION: What is antenna bandwidth? (E9A08)

ANSWER: **The frequency range over which an antenna satisfies a performance requirement**

E9B – Antenna patterns and design: E and H plane patterns; gain as a function of pattern; antenna modeling

Many amateurs use directional antennas because they are said to have "gain." When this term is used, what it means is that a directional antenna will output more power in a particular direction than an antenna that is not directional. This only makes sense; You can't get more power out of an antenna than you put in. Assuming each is driven by the same amount of power, the total amount of radiation emitted by a directional gain antenna is the same as the total amount of radiation emitted from an isotropic antenna.

> QUESTION: How does the total amount of radiation emitted by a directional gain antenna compare with the total amount of radiation emitted from a theoretical isotropic antenna, assuming each is driven by the same amount of power? (E9B07)
>
> ANSWER: **They are the same**

To evaluate the performance of directional antennas, manufacturers will measure the field strength at various points in a circle around the antenna and plot those field strengths, creating a chart called the azimuth antenna radiation pattern. Figure E9-1 is a typical azimuth antenna radiation pattern.

Figure E9-1

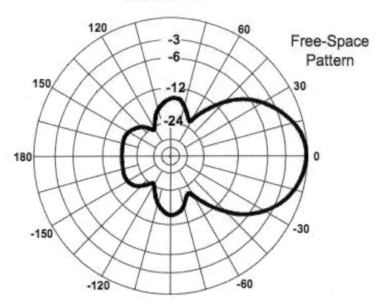

The antenna radiation pattern shows the relative strength of the signal generated by an antenna in its "far field." The far-field of an antenna is the region where the shape of the antenna pattern is independent of distance.

QUESTION: What is the far field of an antenna? (E9B08)

ANSWER: **The region where the shape of the antenna pattern is independent of distance**

From the antenna radiation pattern, we can tell a bunch of things about the antenna. One of them is beamwidth. Beamwidth is a measure of the width of the main lobe of the radiation pattern. To determine the approximate beamwidth in a given plane of a directional antenna, find the two points where the signal strength of the antenna is 3 dB less than maximum and determine the angle between them. In the antenna radiation pattern shown in Figure E9-1, the 3-dB beamwidth is 50 degrees.

QUESTION: In the antenna radiation pattern shown in Figure E9-1, what is the beamwidth? (E9B01)

ANSWER: **50 degrees**

Another parameter that's important for a directional antenna is the front-to-back ratio. The front-to-back ratio is a measure of how directional an antenna is. The higher this ratio, the more directional the antenna. When the radiation pattern is set up so that the forward lobe has a value of 0, as it is in Figure E9-1, the front-to-back ratio is the maximum value of the rear lobe. In the antenna radiation pattern shown in Figure E9-1, the front-to-back ratio is 18 dB.

> QUESTION: In the antenna radiation pattern shown in
> Figure E9-1, what is the front-to-back ratio? (E9B02)

ANSWER: **18 dB**

The front-to-side ratio of a directional antenna is the ratio of the signal transmitted in the forward direction to the signal transmitted perpendicular to that direction. This ratio is normally expressed in dB. In the antenna radiation pattern shown in Figure E9-1, the front-to-side ratio is 14 dB.

> QUESTION: In the antenna radiation pattern shown in
> Figure E9-1, what is the front-to-side ratio? (E9B03)

ANSWER: **14 dB**

Because antennas radiate in three dimensions, the azimuth antenna pattern tells only part of the story. To get a complete picture of antenna performance, you also want to know what the antenna pattern is in the vertical direction. This type of pattern is called the elevation antenna pattern, and is shown in Figure E9-2. This elevation pattern shows four lobes in the forward direction, and the largest, or the lobe with the peak response, has an elevation angle of 7.5 degrees.

Figure E9-2

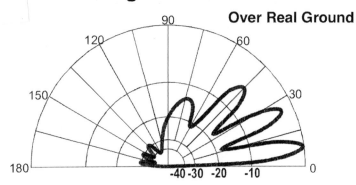

Over Real Ground

QUESTION: What type of antenna pattern is shown in Figure E9-2? (E9B05)

ANSWER: **Elevation**

QUESTION: What is the elevation angle of peak response in the antenna radiation pattern shown in Figure E9-2? (E9B06)

ANSWER: **7.5 degrees**

QUESTION: What is the front-to-back ratio of the radiation pattern shown in Figure E9-2? (E9B04)

ANSWER: **28 dB**

Antenna design

To help design antennas, many amateurs use antenna modeling programs. Antenna modeling programs can provide the following information:

- SWR vs. frequency charts
- Polar plots of the far-field elevation and azimuth patterns
- Antenna gain

The type of computer program technique commonly used for modeling antennas is method of moments. Programs that use the method of moments analysis technique model a wire as a series of segments, each having a uniform value of current.

QUESTION: What type of computer program technique is commonly used for modeling antennas? (E9B09)

ANSWER: **Method of Moments**

QUESTION: What is the principle of a Method of Moments analysis? (E9B10)

ANSWER: **A wire is modeled as a series of segments, each having a uniform value of current**

The more segments your simulation uses, the more accurate the results. The problem with using too many segments, though, is that the program will take a very long time to run. You don't want to use too few segments, though. Decreasing the number of wire segments in an antenna model below the guideline of 10 segments per half-wavelength may cause the computed feed point impedance to be incorrect.

QUESTION: What is a disadvantage of decreasing the number of wire segments in an antenna model below 10 segments per half-wavelength? (E9B11)

ANSWER: **The computed feed point impedance may be incorrect**

E9C – Practical wire antennas; folded dipoles; phased arrays; effects of ground near antennas

There are many ways to put up antennas that are directional. Yagis are directional antennas, but they require a structure, such as a tower, to get them high in the air. One way to get directionality without a tower is to use phased vertical arrays.

In general, the phased vertical array consists of two or more quarter-wave vertical antennas. The radiation pattern that the array will have depends on how you feed the vertical antennas. For example, the radiation pattern of two 1/4-wavelength vertical antennas spaced 1/2-wavelength apart and fed 180 degrees out of phase is a figure-8 oriented along the axis of the array. The radiation pattern of two 1/4-wavelength vertical antennas spaced 1/4-wavelength apart and fed 90 degrees out of phase is a cardioid pattern, and the radiation pattern of two 1/4-wavelength vertical antennas spaced 1/2-wavelength apart and fed in phase is a Figure-8 broadside to the axis of the array.

> QUESTION: What is the radiation pattern of two 1/4-wavelength vertical antennas spaced 1/2-wavelength apart and fed 180 degrees out of phase? (E9C01)
>
> ANSWER: **A figure-8 oriented along the axis of the array**
>
> QUESTION: What is the radiation pattern of two 1/4-wavelength vertical antennas spaced 1/4-wavelength apart and fed 90 degrees out of phase? (E9C02)
>
> ANSWER: **Cardioid**
>
> QUESTION: What is the radiation pattern of two 1/4-wavelength vertical antennas spaced 1/2-wavelength apart and fed in phase? (E9C03)
>
> ANSWER: **A Figure-8 broadside to the axis of the array**

How and where you install an antenna affects its radiation pattern. For example, a vertically polarized antenna has a lower angle of radiation when it is mounted over seawater versus rocky ground.

> QUESTION: How is the far-field elevation pattern of a

vertically polarized antenna affected by being mounted over seawater versus soil? (E9C11)

ANSWER: **The low-angle radiation increases**

Placement also affects horizontally-polarized antennas. For example, the takeoff angle of the main lobe of a horizontally-polarized antenna mounted on the side of a hill will decrease in the downhill direction when compared with the same antenna mounted on flat ground. The radiation pattern of a horizontally polarized 3-element beam antenna will also vary as you change its height above ground. What happens is that the main lobe takeoff angle decreases with increasing height. A low takeoff angle is desirable for making long-distance contacts as it will generally increase the distance that a signal skips off the ionosphere.

QUESTION: How does the performance of a horizontally polarized antenna mounted on the side of a hill compare with the same antenna mounted on flat ground? (E9C14)

ANSWER: **The main lobe takeoff angle decreases in the downhill direction**

QUESTION: How does the radiation pattern of a horizontally polarized 3-element beam antenna vary with increasing height above ground? (E9C13)

ANSWER: **The takeoff angle of the lowest elevation lobe decreases**

Wire antennas

There are many different kinds of wire antennas. Some of the more popular are the long-wire antenna, the folded dipole antenna, the off-center fed dipole antenna, the Zepp antenna, and the G5RV antenna.

The long-wire antenna, as the name implies, is just a long piece of wire, as long as you can make it, strung up as high as you can string it. An antenna tuner is almost always required to match the impedance at the end of the long wire to the 50 Ω output of the transmitter. The radiation pattern of a long-wire antenna is unpredictable, but the lobes align more in the direction of the wire.

QUESTION: What happens to the radiation pattern of an unterminated long wire antenna as the wire length is increased? (E9C04)

ANSWER: **The lobes align more in the direction of the wire**

The folded dipole is a variation on the basic half-wave dipole antenna. A folded dipole antenna is a dipole consisting of one wavelength of wire forming a very thin loop. The approximate feed point impedance at the center of a two-wire folded dipole antenna is 300 ohms. This antenna was very popular when 300 Ω twinlead was used for TV antennas. The reason for this is that 300 Ω was widely available and you could use it for both the antenna and feed line.

QUESTION: What is a folded dipole antenna? (E9C08)

ANSWER: **A half-wave dipole with an additional parallel wire connecting its two ends**

QUESTION: What is the approximate feed point impedance at the center of a two-wire folded dipole antenna? (E9C07)

ANSWER: **300 ohms**

Another popular variation on the half-wave dipole is the off-center fed dipole, or OCFD. An OCFD antenna is a dipole fed approximately 1/3 the way from one end with a 4:1 balun to provide multiband operation. The reason this antenna has become so popular is that it not only provides a good match on its fundamental frequency, but on harmonically-related frequencies as well. An OCFD antenna cut for the 80 m band, for example, will also present a good match on 40 m, 15 m, and 10 m bands.

QUESTION: Which of the following is a type of OCFD antenna? (E9C05)

ANSWER: **A dipole fed approximately 1/3 the way from one end with a 4:1 balun to provide multiband operation**

Zepp antennas are also a half-wavelength long. A Zepp antenna is an end fed dipole antenna. Because the impedance is very high at the feedpoint, the

Zepp antenna uses a quarter-wave length of transmission line to transform the impedance to something closer to the 50 Ω transmitter output impedance. An extended double Zepp antenna is a center-fed 1.25 wavelength antenna (two 5/8 wave elements in phase.

QUESTION: Which of the following describes a Zepp antenna? (E9C10)

ANSWER: **An end-fed dipole antenna**

QUESTION: Which of the following describes an Extended Double Zepp antenna? (E9C12)

ANSWER: **A center-fed 1.25-wavelength antenna (two 5/8-wave elements in phase)**

An example of a wire antenna that is not a half-wavelength long is the G5RV antenna. A G5RV antenna is a multi-band dipole antenna fed with coax and a balun through a selected length of open wire transmission line. The G5RV was originally designed as a single-band, 20m antenna that provided some directionality. Amateurs soon found that they could easily tune this antenna on other frequency bands, and this multi-band capability has made it very popular.

QUESTION: Which of the following describes a G5RV antenna? (E9C09)

ANSWER: **A multi-band dipole antenna fed with coax and a balun through a selected length of open wire transmission line**

Rhombic antennas are large wire antennas that have four sections, each one or more wavelengths long, arranged in a rhombic shape, and fed at one end of the rhomboid. When the end opposite the feedpoint is open, the antenna is bidirectional. Putting a terminating resistor on a rhombic antenna, however, changes the radiation pattern from bidirectional to unidirectional.

QUESTION: What is the effect of adding a terminating resistor to a rhombic antenna? (E9C06)

ANSWER: **It changes the radiation pattern from**

bidirectional to unidirectional

E9D – Yagi antennas; parabolic reflectors; circular polarization; loading coils; top loading; feed point impedance of electrically short antennas; antenna Q; RF grounding

Yagi and parabolic antennas

When designing a Yagi antenna, you might think that the most important parameter is forward gain. What usually occurs if a Yagi antenna is designed solely for maximum forward gain, though, is that the front-to-back ratio decreases. In other words, the antenna becomes more bi-directional than simply directional.

> QUESTION: What usually occurs if a Yagi antenna is designed solely for maximum forward gain? (E9D05)
>
> ANSWER: **The front-to-back ratio decreases**

On the VHF and UHF bands, Yagi antennas are operated horizontally for weak-signal work and vertically for FM operations. In some cases, such as operating satellites, circular polarization is desirable. By arranging two linearly-polarized Yagi antennas perpendicular to each other with the driven elements at the same point on the boom and feeding them 90 degrees out of phase you produce circular polarization. The disadvantage to this approach is, obviously, that you need two antennas, instead of just one to achieve circular polarization.

> QUESTION: How can linearly polarized Yagi antennas be used to produce circular polarization? (E9D02)
>
> ANSWER: **Arrange two Yagis perpendicular to each other with the driven elements at the same point on the boom fed 90 degrees out of phase**

Parabolic antennas are often used at microwave frequencies to direct a signal in a particular direction. The bigger the dish, the higher the gain for a given operating frequency. The gain of an ideal parabolic dish increases by 6 dB when the operating frequency is doubled. The beamwidth is narrower as well.

QUESTION: How much does the gain of an ideal parabolic dish antenna change when the operating frequency is doubled? (E9D01)

ANSWER: **6 dB**

Antenna efficiency, shortened and mobile antennas

Designing an efficient mobile HF antenna is perhaps the toughest job for a radio amateur. More often than not, they are operated below their resonant frequency. From a practical point of view, the antenna's radiation resistance decreases and the capacitive reactance increases as the operating frequency decreases.

That's why most mobile HF antennas use a loading coil to provide a 50 ohm match. The loading coil cancels the capacitive reactance. In effect, loading coils make the radiator of a short vertical antenna look electrically longer.

QUESTION: What happens to feed-point impedance at the base of a fixed length HF mobile antenna when operated below its resonant frequency? (E9D10)

ANSWER: **The radiation resistance decreases and the capacitive reactance increases**

QUESTION: What is the function of a loading coil used as part of an HF mobile antenna? (E9D09)

ANSWER: **To cancel capacitive reactance**

An antenna's loading coil will help you match the feedpoint impedance to 50 ohm coax, but it can't increase the radiation resistance. As a result, short vertical antennas are inherently inefficient. To minimize losses and make them as efficient as possible is to use a high-Q loading coil. That is to say a coil with a high ratio of reactance to resistance. Another thing that you can do is to place the high-Q loading coil near the center of the vertical radiator.

QUESTION: Why should an HF mobile antenna loading coil have a high ratio of reactance to resistance? (E9D04)

ANSWER: **To minimize losses**

QUESTION: Where should a high Q loading coil be placed to minimize losses in a shortened vertical antenna? (E9D03)

ANSWER: **Near the center of the vertical radiator**

One disadvantage of using a loading coil with a short vertical antenna is that it decreases the SWR bandwidth of the antenna. This means that it has to be retuned more frequently than an antenna that doesn't need a loading coil. Not only that, as the Q of an antenna system increases, the SWR bandwidth decreases.

QUESTION: What happens to the SWR bandwidth when one or more loading coils are used to resonate an electrically short antenna? (E9D06)

ANSWER: **It is decreased**

QUESTION: What happens as the Q of an antenna increases? (E9D08)

ANSWER: **SWR bandwidth decreases**

One way that some amateurs improve the radiation efficiency of a short vertical antenna is to use a technique called top loading. This is most often accomplished by using a "capacitance hat" on top of the vertical element.

QUESTION: What is an advantage of using top loading in a shortened HF vertical antenna? (E9D07)

ANSWER: **Improved radiation efficiency**

RF grounding

While much has been written about station grounding, one thing's for sure. A station's safety ground is not adequate as an RF ground. The reason for this is that conductors present different impedances at different frequencies.

Perhaps the best conductor for minimizing losses in a station's RF ground system is wide flat copper strap. The main reason for this is that RF tends to be conducted near the surface of a conductor. The more surface area there is, the lower the impedance to ground, and copper strap normally has many small conductors braided together to maximize surface area.

QUESTION: Which of the following conductors would be best for minimizing losses in a station's RF ground system? (E9D11)

ANSWER: **Wide flat copper strap**

To minimize inductance, it's best to keep the RF ground connection as short as possible. An electrically-short connection to 3 or 4 interconnected ground rods driven into the Earth would provide the best RF ground for your station.

QUESTION: Which of the following would provide the best RF ground for your station? (E9D12)

ANSWER: **An electrically short connection to 3 or 4 interconnected ground rods driven into the Earth**

E9E – Matching: matching antennas to feed lines; phasing lines; power dividers

For many types of antennas, matching the impedance of the antenna to the impedance of the feedline, normally coax, is essential. When a feedline and antenna are mismatched, some of the power you are trying to transmit will be reflected back down the feedline or dissipated in the feedline. The ratio of the amplitude of the reflected wave to the amplitude of the incident wave, or the wave that you're transmitting, is called the reflection coefficient, and it is mathematically related to SWR.

> QUESTION: What parameter describes the interactions at the load end of a mismatched transmission line? (E9E07)
>
> ANSWER: **Reflection coefficient**

To match the impedance of the feedline to the impedance of the antenna, we use a variety of different techniques. The delta matching system matches a high-impedance transmission line to a lower impedance antenna by connecting the line to the driven element in two places spaced a fraction of a wavelength each side of element center. It's called a delta match because when connected this way, the feedline and antenna look like the Greek letter delta.

> QUESTION: What system matches a higher-impedance transmission line to a lower-impedance antenna by connecting the line to the driven element in two places spaced a fraction of a wavelength each side of element center? (E9E01)
>
> ANSWER: **The delta matching system**

The gamma match is an antenna matching system that matches an unbalanced feed line to an antenna by feeding the driven element both at the center of the element and at a fraction of a wavelength to one side of center. The purpose of the series capacitor in a gamma-type antenna matching network is to cancel the inductive reactance of the matching network. The gamma match is an effective method of shunt feeding a grounded tower so it can be used as a vertical antenna.

QUESTION: What is the name of an antenna matching system that matches an unbalanced feed line to an antenna by feeding the driven element both at the center of the element and at a fraction of a wavelength to one side of center? (E9E02)

ANSWER: **The gamma match**

QUESTION: What is the purpose of the series capacitor in a gamma-type antenna matching network? (E9E04)

ANSWER: **To cancel the inductive reactance of the matching network**

QUESTION: Which of the following is used to shunt-feed a grounded tower at its base? (E9E09)

ANSWER: **Gamma match**

The stub match is an antenna matching system that uses a section of transmission line connected in parallel with the feed line at or near the feed point. What the stub does is to add reactance at the feed point. By varying the length of the stub, you can change the reactance that the stub provides to whatever value is needed.

QUESTION: What is the name of the matching system that uses a section of transmission line connected in parallel with the feed line at or near the feed point? (E9E03)

ANSWER: **The stub match**

Many directly-fed Yagi antennas have feedpoint impedances of approximately 20 to 25 ohms. One technique often use to match these antennas to 50-ohm coaxial cable is the hairpin match. To use a hairpin matching system to tune the driven element of a 3-element Yagi, the driven element reactance must be capacitive.

QUESTION: How must an antenna's driven element be tuned to use a hairpin matching system? (E9E05)

ANSWER: **The driven element reactance must be capacitive**

Lengths of 75-ohm coax can also be used to match impedances. For example, inserting a 1/4-wavelength piece of 75-ohm coaxial cable transmission line in series between the antenna terminals and the 50-ohm feed cable is an effective way to match an antenna with a 100-ohm feed point impedance to a 50-ohm coaxial cable feed line. Note that this only works on one band as the length of 75-ohm coax you use will only be 1/4 of a wavelength on one band.

QUESTION: Which of these feed line impedances would be suitable for constructing a quarter-wave Q-section for matching a 100-ohm loop to 50-ohm feed line? (E9E06)

ANSWER: **75 ohms**

QUESTION: Which of these choices is an effective way to match an antenna with a 100-ohm feed point impedance to a 50-ohm coaxial cable feed line? (E9E10)

ANSWER: **Insert a 1/4-wavelength piece of 75-ohm coaxial cable transmission line in series between the antenna terminals and the 50-ohm feed cable**

Another use for coaxial cable is as a phasing line for antennas that have multiple driven elements. The theory here is that by feeding the driven elements out of phase with one another, you can create a directional radiation pattern. A common application for phasing lines is a phased, vertical array.

QUESTION: What is the primary purpose of phasing lines when used with an antenna having multiple driven elements? (E9E11)

ANSWER: **It ensures that each driven element operates in concert with the others to create the desired antenna pattern**

Finally, unless you're going to be doing microwave work, you probably won't need to know about Wilkinson dividers, but here's the information anyway. Wilkinson dividers divide power equally between two 50 ohm loads while maintaining 50 ohm input impedance. They're used mainly in microwave systems.

QUESTION: What is a use for a Wilkinson divider? (E9E08)

ANSWER: **It is used to divide power equally between two 50-ohm loads while maintaining 50-ohm input impedance**

E9F – Transmission lines: characteristics of open and shorted feed lines; coax versus open-wire; velocity factor; electrical length; coaxial cable dielectrics

When setting up your amateur radio station, it's important to know the characteristics of the feed lines you use in your antenna system. For example, did you know that the physical length of a coaxial cable transmission line is shorter than its electrical length? The reason for this is that electrical signals move more slowly in a coaxial cable than in air.

QUESTION: Why is the physical length of a coaxial cable transmission line shorter than its electrical length? (E9F03)

ANSWER: **Electrical signals move more slowly in a coaxial cable than in air**

The term we use to quantify the difference in how fast a wave travels in air versus how fast it travels in a feedline is velocity factor. The velocity factor of a transmission line is the velocity of the wave in the transmission line divided by the velocity of light in a vacuum. The dielectric materials used in the transmission line is one of the biggest factors that determine the velocity factor of a transmission line.

QUESTION: What is the velocity factor of a transmission line? (E9F01)

ANSWER: **The velocity of the wave in the transmission line divided by the velocity of light in a vacuum**

QUESTION: Which of the following has the biggest effect on the velocity factor of a transmission line? (E9F02)

ANSWER: **Dielectric materials used in the line**

Here are some typical velocity factors:
- Solid polyethylene dielectric coaxial transmission line: 0.66
- Foam polyethylene dielectric coaxial transmission line: 0.8
- Air-insulated, parallel-conductor, or open-wire, feedline: 0.98

QUESTION: What is the approximate physical length of a

solid polyethylene dielectric coaxial transmission line that is electrically 1/4 wavelength long at 14.1 MHz? (E9F05)

ANSWER: **3.5 meters**

A 1/4-wavelength at 14.1 MHz is approximately 5.3 m, but the velocity factor of a solid polyethylene dielectric coaxial transmission line is about 0.66, so the physical length will be 5.3 m x 0.66, which is 3.5 meters.

QUESTION: What is the approximate physical length of a foam polyethylene dielectric coaxial transmission line that is electrically 1/4 wavelength long at 7.2 MHz? (E9F09)

ANSWER: **8.3 meters**

A 1/4-wavelength at 7.2 MHz is approximately 10.4 m, but the velocity factor of a foam polyethylene dielectric transmission line is about 0.8, so the physical length will be 10.4 m x 0.8, which is 8.3 meters.

QUESTION: What is the approximate physical length of an air-insulated, parallel conductor transmission line that is electrically 1/2 wavelength long at 14.10 MHz? (E9F06)

ANSWER: **10.6 meters**

A 1/2-wavelength at 14.1 MHz is approximately 10.63 m, but the velocity factor of an air-insulated, parallel conductor transmission line is nearly 1.0, so the physical length will be nearly equal to the electrical length.

In general, coaxial cable transmission lines with a foam dielectric have a higher velocity factor than coaxial cables with a solid dielectric. There are other differences, too. A coaxial cable with a foam dielectric has lower safe operating voltage limits and lower loss per unit of length than a coaxial cable with a solid dielectric.

QUESTION: Which of the following is a significant difference between foam dielectric coaxial cable and solid dielectric cable, assuming all other parameters are the same? (E9F08)

ANSWER: **All these choices are correct**

- Foam dielectric has lower safe operating voltage limits

- Foam dielectric has lower loss per unit of length

- Foam dielectric has higher velocity factor

Arguably, feed line loss is one of the most important characteristic of a transmission line. Obviously, the lower the feed line loss, the stronger the signal your antenna will radiate. Most amateurs use coaxial cable for antenna feed lines, but you should also consider open-wire feedlines or ladder lines. These feed lines have lower losses than most coaxial cable, and certainly have lower loss than small-diameter coaxial cable such as RG-58 at high frequencies.

QUESTION: How does ladder line compare to small-diameter coaxial cable such as RG-58 at 50 MHz? (E9F07)

ANSWER: **Lower loss**

Sometimes we use various lengths of coax to match an antenna system or to filter out frequencies. A 1/8-wavelength transmission line presents an inductive reactance to a generator when the line is shorted at the far end, and this property could be used to match a capacitive load to a transmitter. A 1/8-wavelength transmission line presents a capacitive reactance to a generator when the line is open at the far end. This property could be used to match an inductive load.

QUESTION: What impedance does a 1/8-wavelength transmission line present to a generator when the line is shorted at the far end? (E9F10)

ANSWER: **An inductive reactance**

QUESTION: What impedance does a 1/8-wavelength transmission line present to a generator when the line is open at the far end? (E9F11)

ANSWER: **A capacitive reactance**

A length of transmission line has very different characteristics, depending on whether or not the line is open or shorted at the far end. A 1/4-wavelength transmission line presents a very low impedance to a generator when the line is open at the far end. A 1/4-wavelength transmission line presents a very high impedance to a generator when the line is shorted at the far end. On the other hand, a 1/2-wavelength transmission line that is shorted at the far end presents a very low impedance.

QUESTION: What impedance does a 1/4-wavelength transmission line present to a generator when the line is open at the far end? (E9F12)

ANSWER: **Very low impedance**

QUESTION: What impedance does a 1/4-wavelength transmission line present to a generator when the line is shorted at the far end? (E9F13)

ANSWER: **Very high impedance**

QUESTION: What impedance does a 1/2-wavelength transmission line present to a generator when the line is shorted at the far end? (E9F04)

ANSWER: **Very low impedance**

E9G – The Smith chart

Figure E9-3

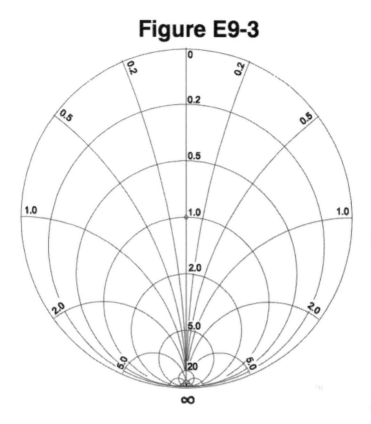

A Smith chart, shown in Figure E9-3 above, is a chart designed to solve transmission line problems graphically. While a complete discussion of the theory behind the Smith Chart is outside the scope of this study guide, a good discussion of the Smith Chart can be found on the ARRL website.

The Smith chart coordinate system is comprised of resistance circles and reactance arcs. The resistance axis is the only straight line on the Smith chart. Points on this axis are pure resistances. In practice, you want to position the chart so that 0 ohms is at the far left, while infinity is at the far right.

QUESTION: What type of coordinate system is used in a Smith chart? (E9G02)

ANSWER: **Resistance circles and reactance arcs**

QUESTION: What are the two families of circles and arcs that make up a Smith chart? (E9G04)

ANSWER: **Resistance and reactance**

QUESTION: On the Smith chart shown in Figure E9-3, what is the only straight line shown? (E9G07)

ANSWER: **The resistance axis**

The arcs on a Smith chart represent points with constant reactance, and the large outer circle on which the reactance arcs terminate is called the reactance axis. Points on the reactance axis have a resistance of 0 ohms. When oriented so that the resistance axis is horizontal, positive reactances are plotted above the resistance axis and negative reactances below.

QUESTION: What do the arcs on a Smith chart represent? (E9G10)

ANSWER: **Points with constant reactance**

QUESTION: On the Smith chart shown in Figure E9-3, what is the name for the large outer circle on which the reactance arcs terminate? (E9G06)

ANSWER: **Reactance axis**

When you work with a Smith Chart, you use resistance and reactance values that are *normalized* to the characteristic impedance of the system. What this means is that if you're working with a 50 ohm transmission line, you'd normally divide the impedances by 50, meaning that a 50 ohm resistance would then be plotted on the resistance axis at the point marked 1.0. A reactance of 50 + j100 would be plotted on the resistance circle going through the prime center where it intersects the reactance arc marked 2.0. The point marked 1.0 on the resistance axis is called the *prime center* of the Smith Chart, so we say that the process of normalization with regard to a Smith chart refers to reassigning impedance values with regard to the prime center.

QUESTION: What is the process of normalization with regard to a Smith chart? (E9G08)

ANSWER: **Reassigning impedance values with regard to the prime center**

Smith Charts are often used for calculating impedance and SWR along a transmission line. When used to calculate SWR, standing-wave ratio circles are often added to the Smith Chart.

QUESTION: Which of the following can be calculated using a Smith chart? (E9G01)

ANSWER: **Impedance along transmission lines**

QUESTION: Which of the following is often determined using a Smith chart? (E9G03)

ANSWER: **Impedance and SWR values in transmission lines**

QUESTION: What third family of circles is often added to a Smith chart during the process of solving problems? (E9G09)

ANSWER: **Standing wave ratio circles**

Another common application for the Smith Chart is to determine the length and position of an impedance matching stub. When using the Smith Chart for this application, remember that the wavelength scales on a Smith chart are calibrated in fractions of transmission line electrical wavelength. When cutting a length of feedline for an impedance matching stub, remember to use the velocity factor of the feedline to find the actual physical length.

QUESTION: Which of the following is a common use for a Smith chart? (E9G05)

ANSWER: **Determine the length and position of an impedance matching stub**

QUESTION: How are the wavelength scales on a Smith chart calibrated? (E9G11)

ANSWER: **In fractions of transmission line electrical**

wavelength

E9H – Receiving Antennas: radio direction finding antennas; Beverage antennas; specialized receiving antennas; long-wire receiving antennas

Many antennas, such as the Beverage antenna, are designed to be receiving antennas only. When constructing a Beverage antennas, make sure that it is one or more wavelengths long to achieve good performance at the desired frequency.

The Beverage antenna is a directional antenna, but it has no gain when compared to a dipole. While directionality is a desirable feature for a receiving antenna, gain often is not, especially on the low bands. The reason for this is that atmospheric noise is so high that gain over a dipole is not important for low band (160 meter and 80 meter) receiving antennas.

> QUESTION: When constructing a Beverage antenna, which of the following factors should be included in the design to achieve good performance at the desired frequency? (E9H01)
>
> ANSWER: **It should be one or more wavelengths long**
>
> QUESTION: Which is generally true for low band (160 meter and 80 meter) receiving antennas? (E9H02)
>
> ANSWER: **Atmospheric noise is so high that gain over a dipole is not important**

Another type of low-noise receiving antenna is the pennant antenna. They are called this because they consist of a triangular loop that looks like a pennant. They are smaller than Beverages, and some designs are even rotatable.

> QUESTION: What is a Pennant antenna? (E9H09)
>
> ANSWER: **A small, vertically oriented receiving antenna consisting of a triangular loop**

The ratio of forward gain to the average gain over the hemisphere in which a directional antenna is pointing is a good measure of how well a receiving antenna works. This is called the receiving directivity factor

(RDF). Pennant antennas have an RDF of about 7.5 dB, while a one-wavelength Beverage antenna has an RDF of about 8.6 dB.

QUESTION: What is Receiving Directivity Factor (RDF)? (E9H03)

ANSWER: **Forward gain compared to average gain over the entire hemisphere**

Direction finding antennas

Direction finding is an activity that's both fun and useful. One of the ways that it's useful is to hunt down noise sources. It can also be used to hunt down stations causing harmful interference.

A variety of directional antennas are used in direction finding, including receiving loop antennas. The main drawback of a wire-loop antenna for direction finding is that it has a bidirectional pattern. Another disadvantage of a receiving loop antenna is that it can have a low output, but the output voltage of a multi-turn receiving loop antenna can be increased by increasing either the number of wire turns in the loop or the area of the loop.

QUESTION: What is the main drawback of a small wire-loop antenna for direction finding? (E9H05)

ANSWER: **It has a bidirectional pattern**

QUESTION: How can the output voltage of a multiple-turn receiving loop antenna be increased? (E9H10)

ANSWER: **By increasing the number of turns and/or the area**

Another way to improve the performance of a loop antenna is to place a grounded electrostatic shield around the loop. This improves the nulls by eliminating unbalanced capacitive couple to the antenna's surroundings.

QUESTION: What is an advantage of placing a grounded electrostatic shield around a small loop direction-finding antenna? (E9H04)

ANSWER: **It eliminates unbalanced capacitive coupling to**

the surroundings, improving the nulls

Sometimes a sense antenna is used with a direction finding antenna. A sense antenna modifies the pattern of a direction-finding (DF) antenna array to provide a null in one direction.

QUESTION: What is the function of a sense antenna? (E9H08)

ANSWER: **It modifies the pattern of a DF antenna array to provide a null in one direction**

Another way to obtain a null in only one direction is to build an antenna array with a cardioid pattern. One way to do this is to build an array with two dipoles fed in quadrature. An antenna with a cardioid pattern has a very sharp single null that makes it useful for direction finding.

QUESTION: What feature of a cardioid pattern antenna makes it useful for direction finding? (E9H11)

ANSWER: **A very sharp single null**

An accessory that is often used in direction finding is an attenuator. Attenuation is useful when direction finding because it prevents receiver overload which reduces the sharpness of the nulls, and thereby, the accuracy of the directional antenna.

QUESTION: Why is RF attenuation used when direction-finding? (E9H07)

ANSWER: **To prevent receiver overload which reduces pattern nulls**

If more than one operator can be mobilized for a direction-finding operation, they could use the triangulation method for finding a noise source or the source of a radio signal. When triangulating a signal source, operators use antenna headings from several different receiving locations to locate it.

QUESTION: What is the triangulation method of direction

finding? (E9H06)

ANSWER: **Antenna headings from several different receiving locations are used to locate the signal source**

E3: RADIO WAVE PROPAGATION

E3A – Electromagnetic waves; Earth-Moon-Earth communications; meteor scatter; microwave tropospheric and scatter propagation; aurora propagation; ionospheric propagation changes over the day; circular polarization

Radio waves are electromagnetic waves meaning that they consist of an electric field and a magnetic field oscillating at right angles to each other. This oscillation is what propels a radio wave through space.

An important characteristic of an electromagnetic wave is its polarization. A wave is said to be vertically polarized if its electric field is perpendicular to the Earth and horizontally polarized if the electric field is parallel to the Earth. Electromagnetic waves with a rotating electric field are said to be circularly polarized.

QUESTION: What is meant by circularly polarized electromagnetic waves? (E3A14)

ANSWER: **Waves with a rotating electric field**

Moon bounce, or Earth-Moon-Earth (EME) communication

One of the more exotic amateur radio activities is Earth-Moon-Earth (EME) communication, sometimes called "moon bounce." As this name implies, radio amateurs actually bounce their signals off the moon. This is the ultimate DX. The approximate maximum separation measured along the surface of the Earth between two stations communicating by EME is 12,000 miles, if the Moon is visible at both stations.

QUESTION: What is the approximate maximum separation

measured along the surface of the Earth between two stations communicating by EME? (E3A01)

ANSWER: **12,000 miles, if the moon is visible by both stations**

Because the signal travels such a long way, you need to do everything you can to avoid signal loss. So, for example, scheduling EME contacts when the Moon is at perigee, which is the point at which the Moon is the closest to Earth. will generally result in the least path loss.

QUESTION: When scheduling EME contacts, which of these conditions will generally result in the least path loss? (E3A03)

ANSWER: **When the moon is at perigee**

One interesting characteristic of an EME signal is libration fading. Libration fading of an EME signal is **a fluttery, irregular fading** caused by the irregular surface of the Moon. Signal peaks can last for up to two seconds on the 2m band, and these peaks can actually help operators make contacts when they would otherwise be impossible.

QUESTION: What characterizes libration fading of an EME signal? (E3A02)

ANSWER: **A fluttery irregular fading**

Meteor scatter

Some amateur radio operators bounce their signals off meteor trails. This type of propagation is called meteor scatter. Meteor scatter propagation is possible because when a meteor strikes the Earth's atmosphere, a cylindrical region of free electrons is formed in the E layer of the ionosphere. Meteor-scatter communications is best in the 28 – 148 MHz frequency range.

QUESTION: When a meteor strikes the Earth's atmosphere, a cylindrical region of free electrons is formed at what layer of the ionosphere? (E3A08)

ANSWER: **The E layer**

QUESTION: Which of the following frequency ranges is most suited for meteor scatter communications? (E3A09)

ANSWER: **28 MHz - 148 MHz**

Microwave tropospheric and scatter propagation

While HF propagation is not affected by weather conditions, the same cannot be said for microwave propagation. For example, temperature inversions can create a path in the atmosphere for microwave propagation. These paths form in the troposphere and are often called tropospheric ducts.

Tropospheric propagation of microwave signals often occurs along warm and cold fronts, and atmospheric ducts capable of propagating microwave signals often form over bodies of water. The typical range for tropospheric propagation of microwave signals is 100 to 300 miles.

Tropospheric propagation is quite predictable. There are even websites that you can visit that will tell you where tropospheric ducts currently exist. These websites include William Hepburn's Radio & TV DX Information Centre (http://www.dxinfocentre.com/tropo.html). This site shows where ducting is occurring on Hepburn maps, which are maps that predict the probability of tropospheric propagation.

QUESTION: Which type of atmospheric structure can create a path for microwave propagation? (E3A10)

ANSWER: **Temperature inversion**

QUESTION: Tropospheric propagation of microwave signals often occurs in association with what phenomenon? (E3A05)

ANSWER: **Warm and cold fronts**

QUESTION: Atmospheric ducts capable of propagating microwave signals often form over what geographic feature? (E3A07)

ANSWER: **Bodies of water**

QUESTION: What is a typical range for tropospheric propagation of microwave signals? (E3A11)

ANSWER: **100 miles to 300 miles**

QUESTION: What do Hepburn maps predict? (E3A04)

ANSWER: **Probability of tropospheric propagation**

Aurora propagation

Another interesting type of propagation is aurora propagation. The cause of auroral activity—sometimes called the Northern Lights or aurora borealis—is the interaction in the E layer of charged particles from the Sun with the Earth's magnetic field. CW is the emission mode that is best for aurora propagation.

QUESTION: What is the cause of auroral activity? (E3A12)

ANSWER: **The interaction in the E layer of charged particles from the Sun with the Earth's magnetic field**

QUESTION: Which of these emission modes is best for auroral propagation? (E3A13)

ANSWER: **CW**

Propagation changes over the day

Understanding how HF signals propagate plays a big role in how successful you will be in making contacts on the HF bands. One thing to note is that propagation changes over a day's time. For example, signals might be strong on the 20 m, 15 m, and 10 m bands in the afternoon, but weaken as the sun sets. Should this occur, switching to a lower frequency HF band might help you restore contact with a DX station.

QUESTION: What might help to restore contact when DX signals become too weak to copy across an entire HF band a few hours after sunset? (E3A06)

ANSWER: **Switch to a lower frequency HF band**

E3B – Transequatorial propagation; long-path; ordinary and extraordinary waves; chordal hop; sporadic E mechanisms

There are many interesting types of propagation that occur on the HF bands. They include transequatorial propagation, long-path propagation, and gray-line propagation.

Transequatorial propagation is propagation between two mid-latitude points at approximately the same distance north and south of the magnetic equator. The approximate maximum range for signals using transequatorial propagation is 5000 miles, and the best time of day for transequatorial propagation is afternoon or early evening.

QUESTION: What is transequatorial propagation? (E3B01)

ANSWER: **Propagation between two mid-latitude points at approximately the same distance north and south of the magnetic equator**

QUESTION: What is the approximate maximum range for signals using transequatorial propagation? (E3B02)

ANSWER: **5000 miles**

QUESTION: What is the best time of day for transequatorial propagation? (E3B03)

ANSWER: **Afternoon or early evening**

Long-path propagation is the type of propagation that occurs when the longer of the two direct paths between stations is better for communications than the shorter path. 160 to 10 meters are the amateur bands that typically support long-path propagation. Although 20 meters is the amateur band that most frequently provides long-path propagation, long-path propagation can occur on any band, 160 meters through 10 meters.

QUESTION: Which of the following amateur bands most frequently provides long-path propagation? (E3B06)

ANSWER: **20 meters**

QUESTION: Which amateur bands typically support long-path propagation? (E3B05)

ANSWER: **160 meters to 10 meters**

Sporadic-E propagation occurs when unusually dense patches of ionization form in the E layer of the ionosphere. Sporadic E propagation can occur at any time of day, and is most likely to occur around the solstices, especially the summer solstice.

QUESTION: At what time of day can sporadic E propagation occur? (E3B11)

ANSWER: **Any time**

QUESTION: At what time of year is sporadic E propagation most likely to occur? (E3B09)

ANSWER: **Around the solstices, especially the summer solstice**

Chordal hop propagation occurs when a radio wave is refracted by the ionosphere such that the refracted wave hits the ionosphere and is refracted a second or third time before hitting the ground. Chordal hop propagation is more desirable than multi-hop propagation that uses the Earth as a reflector because chordal reflections are less lossy than Earth reflections.

QUESTION: What is the primary characteristic of chordal hop propagation? (E3B12)

ANSWER: **Successive ionospheric refractions without an intermediate reflection from the ground**

QUESTION: Why is chordal hop propagation desirable? (E3B10)

ANSWER: **The signal experiences less loss compared to multi-hop using Earth as a reflector**

When a linearly-polarized radio wave enters the ionosphere, it splits into two independent waves, called the ordinary wave and the extraordinary wave, each having slightly different propagation characteristics. When these two waves reemerge from the ionosphere, instead of being linearly polarized like the radio wave that entered the ionosphere, the ordinary and extraordinary waves are now elliptically polarized.

QUESTION: What happens to linearly polarized radio waves that split into ordinary and extraordinary waves in the ionosphere? (E3B07)

ANSWER: **They become elliptically polarized**

QUESTION: What is meant by the terms "extraordinary" and "ordinary" waves? (E3B04)

ANSWER: **Independent waves created in the ionosphere that are elliptically polarized**

E3C – Radio horizon; ground wave; propagation prediction techniques and modeling; effects of space weather parameters on propagation

VHF/UHF propagation is mostly "line of sight," meaning that without any objects to reflect the radio waves, they will travel directly from the transmitter to the receiver. In practice, the distance that a VHF/UHF radio wave will travel is slightly longer than the line-of-sight distance. We call this distance the "radio horizon" or "radio-path horizon," and it's about 15% longer than the line-of-sight distance. The radio-path horizon distance extends beyond the geometric horizon because of downward bending due to density variations in the atmosphere.

QUESTION: By how much does the VHF/UHF radio horizon distance exceed the geometric horizon? (E3C06)

ANSWER: **By approximately 15 percent of the distance**

QUESTION: Why does the radio-path horizon distance exceed the geometric horizon? (E3C14)

ANSWER: **Downward bending due to density variations in the atmosphere**

Amateur radio operators may sometimes use ground-wave propagation to communicate. One important thing to know about this type of propagation is that the maximum distance of ground-wave propagation decreases when the signal frequency is increased. Vertical polarization is the best type of polarization for ground-wave propagation. So, if you really want to make a contact via ground wave, use a vertical antenna on the 160m band.

QUESTION: How does the maximum range of ground-wave propagation change when the signal frequency is increased? (E3C12)

ANSWER: **It decreases**

QUESTION: What type of polarization is best for ground-wave propagation? (E3C13)

ANSWER: **Vertical**

Prediction techniques and modeling

If you're interesting in contacting distant stations on the HF bands, it's very advantageous to know the propagation conditions for a particular signal path. That's why many hams use propagation prediction software to choose what frequency bands to use. One of these software packages is called VOACAP, because it was developed by engineers at the Voice of America (VOA). VOACAP software models HF propagation.

QUESTION: What does VOACAP software model? (E3C11)

ANSWER: **HF propagation**

Often, software packages that model HF propagation use a technique called ray tracing. Ray tracing models a radio wave's path through the ionosphere.

QUESTION: What does the radio communication term "ray tracing" describe? (E3C01)

ANSWER: **Modeling a radio wave's path through the ionosphere**

Propagation prediction software uses data such as the A index and K index to model propagation. Both of these provide a measure of geomagnetic activity, which affects HF propagation. A rising A or K index indicates increasing disruption of the geomagnetic field, and generally means that HF propagation will be poor. Polar paths are most likely to experience high levels of absorption when the A index or K index is elevated.

QUESTION: What is indicated by a rising A or K index? (E3C02)

ANSWER: **Increasing disruption of the geomagnetic field**

QUESTION: Which of the following signal paths is most likely to experience high levels of absorption when the A index or K index is elevated? (E3C03)

ANSWER: **Polar**

The interplanetary magnetic field has a very strong affect on HF propagation. The value of Bz (B sub Z) represents the direction and strength of the interplanetary magnetic field. A southward orientation of Bz (B sub z) increases the likelihood that incoming particles from the Sun will cause disturbed conditions. HF propagation is generally poor when Bz is oriented southward and geomagnetic conditions are disturbed.

QUESTION: What does the value of Bz (B sub Z) represent? (E3C04)

ANSWER: **Direction and strength of the interplanetary magnetic field**

QUESTION: What orientation of Bz (B sub z) increases the likelihood that incoming particles from the sun will cause disturbed conditions? (E3C05)

ANSWER: **Southward**

Space weather parameters and amateur radio

Because solar radiation creates the ionosphere, solar activity has a great impact on radio wave propagation. These conditions are often referred to as space weather.

Solar flares, for example, emit an enormous amount of radiation. Depending on how much radiation they emit, the effect on HF propagation can be good or bad. If the Earth receives only enough radiation to increase ionization in the upper layers of the ionosphere, HF propagation is improved.

If the level of radiation is higher, the lower levels of the ionosphere could become more energized. When this happens, they absorb more RF energy, and HF propagation is poor. A sudden rise in radio background noise indicates that a solar flare has occurred.

QUESTION: What might be indicated by a sudden rise in radio background noise across a large portion of the HF spectrum? (E3C15)

ANSWER: **A solar flare has occurred**

Solar flares are categorized by intensity. Class A solar flares are the least intense. Class X is the descriptor that indicates the greatest solar flare intensity. In between Class A and Class X are Class B, Class C, and Class

M. Within each class, solar flares are assigned a value from 1 – 9. An X3 flare is 50% more intense than an X2 flare.

QUESTION: Which of the following descriptors indicates the greatest solar flare intensity? (E3C07)

ANSWER: **Class X**

QUESTION: How does the intensity of an X3 flare compare to that of an X2 flare? (E3C09)

ANSWER: **50 percent greater**

The National Oceanic and Atmospheric Administration (NOAA) has developed what they call Space Weather Scales to communicate to the general public the current and future space weather conditions and their possible effects on people and systems. The G scale indicates geomagnetic conditions. The space weather term G5 means an extreme geomagnetic storm.

QUESTION: What does the space weather term G5 mean? (E3C08)

ANSWER: **An extreme geomagnetic storm**

Sunspots are often used to predict HF propagation conditions. The more sunspots, the better HF propagation is. Parameter 304A may, however, be an even better indicator of radio conditions. The 304A solar parameter measures UV emissions at 304 angstroms, and these emissions are proportional to the solar flux index. These UV emissions are one of the principle causes of F2 layer ionization.

QUESTION: What does the 304A solar parameter measure? (E3C10)

ANSWER: **UV emissions at 304 angstroms, correlated to the solar flux index**

E4: AMATEUR PRACTICES

E4A – Test equipment: analog and digital instruments; spectrum analyzers; antenna analyzers; oscilloscopes; RF measurements; computer-aided measurements

An instrument that amateur radio operators frequently use when experimenting or when debugging equipment is the oscilloscope, or simply just "scope." Oscilloscopes have become more common in amateur radio shacks as prices have fallen, and the technology has moved from analog to digital.

One of the most important oscilloscope specifications is its bandwidth. The bandwidth of an oscilloscope determines the maximum frequency at which the oscilloscope can accurately measure a signal. Several factors determine the highest frequency signal that can be accurately displayed on a digital oscilloscope, including the characteristics of the analog signal processing circuits and the sampling rate of the scope's analog-to-digital converter.

> QUESTION: Which of the following limits the highest frequency signal that can be accurately displayed on a digital oscilloscope? (E4A01)
>
> ANSWER: **Sampling rate of the analog-to-digital converter**

While digital scopes have many advantages over analog scopes, you have to know how to use them properly. For example, because digital oscilloscopes sample an input signal at discrete time intervals, it is possible to fool them into displaying an incorrect waveform. This phenomenon is called aliasing. If you set the time base too slow, the scope may display a false, jittery version of the input signal.

QUESTION: What is the effect of aliasing on a digital oscilloscope caused by setting the time base too slow? (E4A06)

ANSWER: **A false, jittery low-frequency version of the signal is displayed**

Oscilloscope probes

When making measurements at RF frequencies, it's important to connect the probe's ground connection as close to the location of the measurement as possible. Keeping the signal ground connection as short as possible reduces the noise picked up by the probe and reduces the inductance of the connection, which in turn, makes the measurement more accurate.

QUESTION: Which of the following is good practice when using an oscilloscope probe? (E4A09)

ANSWER: **Keep the signal ground connection of the probe as short as possible**

Good quality passive oscilloscope probes have an adjustable capacitor in them that needs to be adjusted so that the probe capacitive reactance is at least nine times the scope input capacitive reactance. When this capacitor is adjusted properly, we say that the probe is properly compensated, and the scope will display the waveform with as little distortion as possible.

Most oscilloscopes have a special square-wave output specifically for the purpose of compensating probes. To adjust the compensation, you connect the probe to this output and then adjust the probe until the horizontal portions of the displayed wave are as nearly flat as possible.

QUESTION: How is the compensation of an oscilloscope probe typically adjusted? (E4A04)

ANSWER: **A square wave is displayed and the probe is adjusted until the horizontal portions of the displayed wave are as nearly flat as possible**

Spectrum analyzers

While oscilloscopes display the amplitude of a signal over time, spectrum analyzers display the amplitude of the frequency components of a signal. As shown in the figure below, the horizontal axis of an oscilloscope display represents time, while the horizontal axis of a spectrum analyzer display represents frequency. For both instruments, the vertical axis represent the amplitude of the signal being measured.

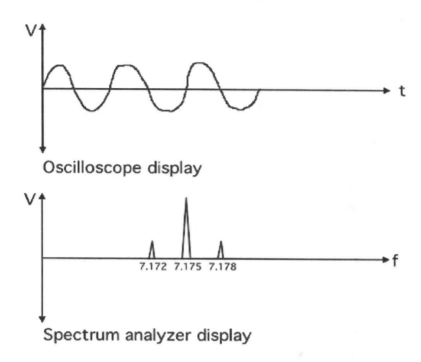

Spectrum analyzers are very useful for troubleshooting problems. For example, a spectrum analyzer is used to display spurious signals or intermodulation distortion products generated by an SSB transmitter.

QUESTION: Which of the following parameters does a spectrum analyzer display on the vertical and horizontal axes? (E4A02)

ANSWER: **RF amplitude and frequency**

QUESTION: Which of the following test instruments is used to display spurious signals and/or intermodulation distortion products generated by an SSB transmitter? (E4A03)

ANSWER: **A spectrum analyzer**

Antenna analyzers

One of the instruments that I think every amateur radio operator should have (or at least have access to) is the antenna analyzer. Antenna analyzers are versatile instruments that allow amateur radio operators to easily make antenna measurements, as well as other impedance measurements. They can even be used as low power RF signal generators. One of the most common uses for an antenna analyzer is measuring the SWR of an antenna system.

An advantage of using an antenna analyzer compared to an SWR bridge to measure antenna SWR is that antenna analyzers do not need an external RF source. What this means is that you don't need to connect your transmitter to the antenna to tune it. This is because antenna analyzers have internal RF signal generators.

You can also make related measurements, such as the antenna resonant frequency and feed point impedance with an antenna analyzer. To make these measurements you connect the antenna feed line directly to the analyzer's connector.

> QUESTION: Which of the following measures SWR? (E4A08)
>
> ANSWER: **An antenna analyzer**
>
> QUESTION: Which of the following is an advantage of using an antenna analyzer compared to an SWR bridge to measure antenna SWR? (E4A07)
>
> ANSWER: **Antenna analyzers do not need an external RF source**
>
> QUESTION: How should an antenna analyzer be connected when measuring antenna resonance and feed point impedance? (E4A11)
>
> ANSWER: **Connect the antenna feed line directly to the analyzer's connector**

Frequency counters, logic analyzers

To measure the frequency of a signal, you use an instrument called a frequency counter. When selecting a frequency counter, an important specification is the maximum frequency. If you want to measure the frequency of a signal whose frequency is higher than the maximum frequency of your counter, you might use a prescaler. A prescaler divides a higher frequency signal so a low-frequency counter can display the input frequency.

QUESTION: What is the purpose of the prescaler function on a frequency counter? (E4A05)

ANSWER: **It divides a higher frequency signal so a low-frequency counter can display the input frequency**

The proper operation of a digital circuit depends on the output state of many digital ICs at specific times. To ensure that a circuit is working properly, or to troubleshoot a circuit, you may want to use a logic analyzer because it displays multiple digital signal states simultaneously.

QUESTION: Which of the following displays multiple digital signal states simultaneously? (E4A10)

ANSWER: **Logic analyzer**

E4B – Measurement technique and limitations: instrument accuracy and performance limitations; probes; techniques to minimize errors; measurement of Q; instrument calibration; S parameters; vector network analyzers

When making measurements, you should keep in mind that test instruments are not 100% accurate. What that means is that the instrument reading is not exactly the value of the parameter you're measuring. The reading is always going to be off by some amount.

Let's consider frequency counters. Frequency counters are useful instruments for measuring the output frequency of amateur radio transceivers. While a number of different factors can affect the accuracy of an instrument, time base accuracy is the factor that most affects the accuracy of a frequency counter. The time base accuracy of most inexpensive frequency counters is about 1 part per million, or 1 ppm. So, if you were measuring a frequency of 146.520 MHz with a frequency counter with a specified accuracy of +/- 1.0 ppm, the measured frequency could vary by as much as 146.52 Hz, meaning that the frequency counter could as low as 146.519853 MHz or as high as 146.520147 MHz.

QUESTION: Which of the following factors most affects the accuracy of a frequency counter? (E4B01)

ANSWER: **Time base accuracy**

Voltmeters

Probably the most common test instrument in an amateur radio station is a voltmeter. The voltmeter may be part of a digital multimeter (DMM) or volt-ohm meter (VOM). DMMs have the advantage of high input impedance. The higher the input impedance, the less effect the meter will have on the measurement.

The input impedance of a VOM is calculated using the VOM's sensitivity expressed in ohms per volt. The full scale reading of the voltmeter multiplied by its ohms per volt rating will provide the input impedance of the voltmeter. A higher ohms per volt rating means that it will have a higher input impedance than a meter with a lower ohms per volt rating.

QUESTION: What is the significance of voltmeter sensitivity expressed in ohms per volt? (E4B02)

ANSWER: **The full scale reading of the voltmeter multiplied by its ohms per volt rating will indicate the input impedance of the voltmeter**

RF measurements

Directional power meters and RF ammeters are two instruments that you can use to make antenna measurements. With a directional power meter, you could measure the forward power and reflected power and then figure out how much power is being delivered to the load and calculate the SWR of the antenna system. For example, if you measure 100 watts of forward power and 25 watts reflected power with a directional wattmeter when you connect it between a transmitter and a terminating load, then you know that 75 watts is being absorbed by the load. If your load is an antenna, you can then calculate the SWR of the antenna system using these values.

QUESTION: How much power is being absorbed by the load when a directional power meter connected between a transmitter and a terminating load reads 100 watts forward power and 25 watts reflected power? (E4B06)

ANSWER: **75 watts**

With an RF ammeter, you measure the RF current flowing in an antenna system. If you connect an RF ammeter in series with the antenna feed line of a transmitter, you should find that the RF current increases as the transmitter is tuned to resonance. This means there is more power going into the antenna.

QUESTION: What is indicated if the current reading on an RF ammeter placed in series with the antenna feed line of a transmitter increases as the transmitter is tuned to resonance? (E4B09)

ANSWER: **There is more power going into the antenna**

For some designs, you'll want to know not only the resonant frequency of a circuit but also the quality factor, or Q, of the circuit. As we noted in the chapter on antennas, circuits with a high Q have a narrower bandwidth than circuits with a lower Q. Determining the bandwidth of a series-tuned circuit's frequency response can, therefore, be used to measure the Q of the circuit.

QUESTION: Which of the following can be used to measure the Q of a series-tuned circuit? (E4B08)

ANSWER: **The bandwidth of the circuit's frequency response**

A test that's often used to measure intermodulation distortion in an SSB transmitter is called the two-tone test. To perform this test, you modulate the transmitter with two audio frequency signals that are not harmonically related audio frequencies and observe the RF output with a spectrum analyzer. The instrument that provides the audio frequency signals is called, oddly enough, a two-tone generator, and typically, these generators provide tones of 700 Hz and 1,900 Hz simultaneously.

QUESTION: Which of the following methods measures intermodulation distortion in an SSB transmitter? (E4B10)

ANSWER: **Modulate the transmitter using two AF signals having non-harmonically related frequencies and observe the RF output with a spectrum analyzer**

Vector network analyzers, S parameters

An instrument that you might use to make these measurements is a vector network analyzer. As with any instrument, you first need to ensure that it is calibrated properly. Three test loads used to calibrate a standard RF vector network analyzer are short circuit, open circuit, and 50 ohms.

QUESTION: Which of the following can be measured with a vector network analyzer? (E4B11)

ANSWER: **All these choices are correct**

- Input impedance

- Output impedance

- Reflection coefficient

QUESTION: What three test loads are used to calibrate an RF vector network analyzer? (E4B05)

ANSWER: **Short circuit, open circuit, and 50 ohms**

You can also use vector network analyzer to measure S-parameters, or scattering parameters. S-parameters describe the behavior of RF devices under linear conditions. Each parameter is typically characterized by magnitude, decibel and phase. The subscripts of S parameters represent the port or ports at which measurements are made. The S parameter that is equivalent to forward gain is S21. The S parameter that represents return loss or SWR is S11.

QUESTION: What do the subscripts of S parameters represent? (E4B07)

ANSWER: **The port or ports at which measurements are made**

QUESTION: Which S parameter is equivalent to forward gain? (E4B03)

ANSWER: **S21**

QUESTION: Which S parameter represents input port return loss or reflection coefficient (equivalent to VSWR)? (E4B04)

ANSWER: **S11**

⁞ – Receiver performance characteristics: phase noise, noise floor, image rejection, MDS, signal-to-noise ratio, noise figure, reciprocal mixing; selectivity; effects of SDR receiver non-linearity; use of attenuators at low frequencies

In the past, sensitivity was one of the most important receiver performance specifications. Today, instead of sensitivity, we speak of a receiver's minimum discernible signal, or MDS. This is the weakest signal that a receiver will detect. One parameter that affects a receiver's MDS is the noise figure. The noise figure of a receiver is the ratio in dB of the noise generated by the receiver compared to the theoretical minimum noise.

QUESTION: What does the MDS of a receiver represent? (E4C07)

ANSWER: **The minimum discernible signal**

QUESTION: What is the noise figure of a receiver? (E4C04)

ANSWER: **The ratio in dB of the noise generated by the receiver to the theoretical minimum noise**

A related specification is the noise floor. A noise floor of -174 dBm/Hz, is the theoretical noise at the input of a perfect receiver at room temperature. If a CW receiver with the AGC off has an equivalent input noise power density of -174 dBm/Hz, the level of an unmodulated carrier input to this receiver would have to be -148 dBm to yield an audio output SNR of 0 dB in a 400 Hz noise bandwidth.

QUESTION: What does a receiver noise floor of -174 dBm represent? (E4C05)

ANSWER: **The theoretical noise in a 1 Hz bandwidth at the input of a perfect receiver at room temperature**

QUESTION: A CW receiver with the AGC off has an equivalent input noise power density of -174 dBm/Hz. What would be the level of an unmodulated carrier input to this receiver that would yield an audio output SNR of 0 dB in a

400 Hz noise bandwidth? (E4C06)

ANSWER: **-148 dBm**

Modern transceivers use digital signal processing (DSP) to filter out noise and eliminate interference at one of the IF stages. Instead of just a few fixed bandwidths, DSP techniques allow an operator to select from a wide variety of bandwidths, enabling the operator to select a receive bandwidth that's optimum for the type of signal he or she is receiving. This maximizes the signal to noise ratio and minimizes interference.

QUESTION: What is an advantage of having a variety of receiver IF bandwidths from which to select? (E4C10)

ANSWER: **Receive bandwidth can be set to match the modulation bandwidth, maximizing signal-to-noise ratio and minimizing interference**

Although modern transceivers have sophisticated DSP filters, many also use roofing filters to improve receiver performance. Roofing filters filter incoming signals before the first intermediate frequency (IF) stage, blocking strong signals near the receive frequency that could cause overloading and distortion in the following amplifier stages. In doing so, a narrow-band roofing filter improves a receiver's dynamic range.

QUESTION: How does a narrow-band roofing filter affect receiver performance? (E4C13)

ANSWER: **It improves dynamic range by attenuating strong signals near the receive frequency**

Back in the day, when superheterodyne receivers had intermediate frequencies in the 400 – 500 kHz range, image rejection was a problem. If there was a strong signal present on a frequency about two times the IF away from the receive frequency, you might hear that signal. For example, you might hear a strong signal transmitting on 15.210 MHz on a receiver that has a 455 kHz IF frequency and is tuned to 14.300 MHz.

QUESTION: What transmit frequency might generate an image response signal in a receiver tuned to 14.300 MHz and that uses a 455 kHz IF frequency? (E4C14)

ANSWER: **15.210 MHz**

One way to improve a receiver's image rejection is to select a higher IF frequency. Doing so makes it easier for front-end circuitry, such as filters and pre-selectors, to eliminate image responses. A front-end filter or pre-selector of a receiver can also be effective in eliminating out-of-band signal interference.

QUESTION: Which of the following choices is a good reason for selecting a high frequency for the design of the IF in a superheterodyne HF or VHF communications receiver? (E4C09)

ANSWER: **Easier for front-end circuitry to eliminate image responses**

QUESTION: Which of the following receiver circuits can be effective in eliminating interference from strong out-of-band signals? (E4C02)

ANSWER: **A front-end filter or pre-selector**

Because most modern transceivers use digital techniques to generate a local oscillator signal to tune a receiver, synthesizer phase noise might be a problem. An effect of excessive phase noise in the local oscillator section of a receiver is that it can combine with strong signals on nearby frequencies to generate interference. The process whereby local oscillator phase noise combines with adjacent strong signals to create interference to desired signals is called reciprocal mixing.

QUESTION: What is an effect of excessive phase noise in a receiver's local oscillator? (E4C01)

ANSWER: **It can combine with strong signals on nearby frequencies to generate interference**

QUESTION: What is reciprocal mixing? (E4C15)

ANSWER: **Local oscillator phase noise mixing with adjacent strong signals to create interference to desired signals**

Software-defined radio (SDR) is becoming more popular in amateur radio. It is, therefore, necessary to know something about SDR receiver characteristics. For example, an SDR receiver's analog-to-digital converter (ADC) sample width in bits has the largest effect on an SDR receiver's linearity. An SDR receiver is overloaded when input signals exceeds the reference voltage of the analog-to-digital converter. When this happens, the ADC outputs the maximum value no matter what the input value is.

QUESTION: Which of the following has the largest effect on an SDR receiver's dynamic range? (E4C12)

ANSWER: **Analog-to-digital converter sample width in bits**

QUESTION: An SDR receiver is overloaded when input signals exceed what level? (E4C08)

ANSWER: **The reference voltage of the analog-to-digital converter**

Most transceivers have built-in attenuators to reduce receiver overload. Although attenuators reduce the strength of incoming signals, they have little or no impact on signal-to-noise ratio because atmospheric noise is a much bigger contributor to the overall noise level than internally generated noise, and the attenuator attenuates atmospheric noise as much as it does the incoming signal.

QUESTION: Why can an attenuator be used to reduce receiver overload on the lower frequency HF bands with little or no impact on signal-to-noise ratio? (E4C11)

ANSWER: **Atmospheric noise is generally greater than internally generated noise even after attenuation**

Finally, here is a miscellaneous question on FM receiver performance characteristics.

QUESTION: What is the term for the suppression in an FM receiver of one signal by another stronger signal on the same frequency? (E4C03)

ANSWER: **Capture effect**

E4D – Receiver performance characteristics: blocking dynamic range; intermodulation and cross-modulation interference; third-order intercept; desensitization; preselector

One of the most commonly mentioned HF receiver specifications is blocking dynamic range. It is a measure of how strong an interfering signal has to be, referenced to the noise floor of the receiver, to reduce the strength of an incoming signal by 1 dB. The blocking dynamic range of a receiver is the difference in dB between the noise floor and the level of an incoming signal that will cause 1 dB of gain compression.

QUESTION: What is meant by the blocking dynamic range of a receiver? (E4D01)

ANSWER: **The difference in dB between the noise floor and the level of an incoming signal that will cause 1 dB of gain compression**

Intermodulation is the term for unwanted signals generated by the mixing of two or more signals and is the result of circuits or devices being nonlinear. A measure of the nonlinearity of a receiver is the third-order intercept level. The third-order intercept level is the level at which a third-order intermodulation product will reach the level of the signal being received. So, for example, if a receiver is said to have a third-order intercept level of 40 dBm it means that a pair of 40 dBm input signals will theoretically generate a third-order intermodulation product with the same level as the input signals. The higher the third-order intercept level, the better the receiver. Compared to other intermodulation products, odd-order intermodulation products created within a receiver are of particular interest because the odd-order product of two signals in the band of interest is also likely to be within the band.

QUESTION: What is the term for spurious signals generated by the combination of two or more signals in a non-linear device or circuit? (E4D06)

ANSWER: **Intermodulation**

QUESTION: What causes intermodulation in an electronic

circuit? (E4D08)

ANSWER: **Nonlinear circuits or devices**

QUESTION: What does a third-order intercept level of 40 dBm mean with respect to receiver performance? (E4D10)

ANSWER: **A pair of 40 dBm input signals will theoretically generate a third-order intermodulation product that has the same output amplitude as either of the input signals**

QUESTION: Why are odd-order intermodulation products, created within a receiver, of particular interest compared to other products? (E4D11)

ANSWER: **Odd-order products of two signals in the band of interest are also likely to be within the band**

Strong nearby signals can also reduce the sensitivity of a receiver. This reduction in receiver sensitivity is called desensitization. Another cause of desensitization is poor dynamic range. Poor dynamic range may also cause the receiver to produce spurious signals by cross modulation. One way to reduce the likelihood of receiver desensitization is to decrease the RF bandwidth of the receiver. This reduces the likelihood of a strong signal appearing in the receiver's passband.

QUESTION: What is the term for the reduction in receiver sensitivity caused by a strong signal near the received frequency? (E4D12)

ANSWER: **Desensitization**

QUESTION: Which of the following describes problems caused by poor dynamic range in a receiver? (E4D02)

ANSWER: **Spurious signals caused by cross-modulation and desensitization from strong adjacent signals**

QUESTION: Which of the following reduces the likelihood of receiver desensitization? (E4D07)

ANSWER: **Decrease the RF bandwidth of the receiver**

A preselector might help in some cases. The purpose of the preselector in a communications receiver is to increase rejection of unwanted signals outside of a desired band.

QUESTION: What is the purpose of the preselector in a communications receiver? (E4D09)

ANSWER: **To increase rejection of signals outside the desired band**

Intermodulation can also happen in the final amplifiers of amateur radio transmitters. For example, intermodulation interference between two repeaters often occurs when the repeaters are in close proximity and the signals mix in the final amplifier of one or both transmitters. For example, if you had a receiver tuned to 146.70 MHz and a nearby station transmits on 146.52 MHz, you might hear signals on 146.34 MHz and 146.61 MHz as well. Here's how the signals might combine:

$$2 \times 146.52 \text{ MHz} - 146.34 \text{ MHz} = 146.70 \text{ MHz and}$$

$$2 \times 146.61 \text{ MHz} - 146.52 \text{ MHz} = 146.70 \text{ MHz}$$

QUESTION: How can intermodulation interference between two repeaters occur? (E4D03)

ANSWER: **When the repeaters are in close proximity and the signals mix in the final amplifier of one or both transmitters**

QUESTION: What transmitter frequencies would cause an intermodulation-product signal in a receiver tuned to 146.70 MHz when a nearby station transmits on 146.52 MHz? (E4D05)

ANSWER: **146.34 MHz and 146.61 MHz**

A properly terminated circulator at the output of the transmitter may reduce or eliminate intermodulation interference in a repeater caused by another transmitter operating in close proximity. The circulator reduces intermodulation distortion because it helps to reduce the amount of energy from nearby transmitters that might get into a repeater's final amplifier.

QUESTION: Which of the following may reduce or eliminate intermodulation interference in a repeater caused by another transmitter operating in close proximity? (E4D04)

ANSWER: **A properly terminated circulator at the output of the repeater's transmitter**

E4E – Noise suppression and interference: system noise; electrical appliance noise; line noise; locating noise sources; DSP noise reduction; noise blankers; grounding for signals; common mode currents

Noise is often a real problem for radio amateurs. Fortunately, by understanding how noise is generated and how to reduce or eliminate it, noise can be tamed.

Atmospheric noise is naturally-occurring noise that appears across a wide bandwidth. To help you copy signals when there's a lot of atmospheric noise, or any wide bandwidth noise, you can often use a receiver's noise blanker. One undesirable effect that can occur when using a receiver's IF noise blanker is that nearby signals may appear to be excessively wide even if they meet emission standards.

QUESTION: Which of the following signals might a receiver noise blanker be able to remove from desired signals? (E4E03)

ANSWER: **Signals that appear across a wide bandwidth**

QUESTION: What undesirable effect can occur when using an IF noise blanker? (E4E09)

ANSWER: **Nearby signals may appear to be excessively wide even if they meet emission standards**

Many modern receivers now use digital signal processing (DSP) filters to eliminate noise. The types of receiver noise that can often be reduced with a DSP noise filter, include broadband white noise, ignition noise, and power line noise.

QUESTION: Which of the following types of noise can often be reduced with a digital signal processing noise filter? (E4E02)

ANSWER: **All these choices are correct**

• Broadband white noise

- Ignition noise

- Power line noise

Some receivers with DSP filter have an automatic notch filter, or ANF. An automatic notch filter recognizes interfering signals in the passband and attempts to set the notch to filter out that signal. When receiving CW signals, however, the filter may remove the CW signal as well as the interfering carrier.

QUESTION: What problem can occur when using an automatic notch filter (ANF) to remove interfering carriers while receiving CW signals? (E4E01)

ANSWER: **Removal of the CW signal as well as the interfering carrier**

While filters can be very effective at reducing noise, it is often better to figure out what is generating the noise and take steps to reduce or eliminate the amount of noise generated in the first place. Loud roaring or buzzing AC line interference that comes and goes at intervals could be caused by arcing contacts in a thermostatically controlled device, a defective doorbell or doorbell transformer inside a nearby residence, or a malfunctioning illuminated advertising display. To determine if the AC line noise interference is being generated within your home turn off the AC power line main circuit breaker and listening on a battery operated radio to see if the noise goes away. If by doing this you determine that an electric motor is a problem, noise from an electric motor can be suppressed by installing a bypass capacitor across the motor leads.

QUESTION: What might be the cause of a loud roaring or buzzing AC line interference that comes and goes at intervals? (E4E10)

ANSWER: **All these choices are correct**

- Arcing contacts in a thermostatically controlled device

- A defective doorbell or doorbell transformer inside a nearby residence

- A malfunctioning illuminated advertising display

QUESTION: How can radio frequency interference from an AC motor be suppressed? (E4E05)

ANSWER: **By installing a bypass capacitor in series with the motor leads**

Sometimes your own equipment may be the cause of received noise. Cables in an amateur radio station, for example, can radiate or pick up interference. Common mode currents are the culprits. Common mode current is current that flows equally on all conductors of an unshielded multi-conductor cable. Common mode current on the shield and conductors can also cause shielded cables to radiate or receive interference. To eliminate this interference, make sure to ground the shield at one end of the cable.

QUESTION: Which of the following can cause shielded cables to radiate or receive interference? (E4E07)

ANSWER: **Common-mode currents on the shield and conductors**

QUESTION: What current flows equally on all conductors of an unshielded multi-conductor cable? (E4E08)

ANSWER: **Common-mode current**

The main source of noise in an automobile is the alternator. Conducted and radiated noise caused by an automobile alternator can be suppressed by connecting the radio's power leads directly to the battery and by installing coaxial capacitors in line with the alternator leads. The capacitors help filter out the noise, and short, direct leads to the battery help prevent noise pickup.

QUESTION: How can conducted and radiated noise caused by an automobile alternator be suppressed? (E4E04)

ANSWER: **By connecting the radio's power leads directly to the battery and by installing coaxial capacitors in line with the alternator leads**

Personal computers and other digital devices can also generate noise. One type of electrical interference that might be caused by the operation of a nearby personal computer is the appearance of unstable modulated or unmodulated signals at specific frequencies.

QUESTION: What is one type of electrical interference that might be caused by a nearby personal computer? (E4E06)

ANSWER: **The appearance of unstable modulated or unmodulated signals at specific frequencies**

Noise can even be generated by the most unlikely things. For example, if you are hearing local AM broadcast band signals on one or more of the MF or HF ham bands it's possible that nearby corroded metal joints are mixing and re-radiating the broadcast signals.

QUESTION: What could cause local AM broadcast band signals to combine to generate spurious signals in the MF or HF bands? (E4E11)

ANSWER: **Nearby corroded metal joints are mixing and re-radiating the broadcast signals**

E2: OPERATING PROCEDURES

E2A – Amateur radio in space: amateur satellites; orbital mechanics; frequencies and modes; satellite hardware; satellite operations

Making contacts via amateur satellites is a very popular amateur radio activity. There's even an organization dedicated to launching and operating amateur radio satellites—AMSAT (www.amsat.org).

Perhaps the most important thing you need to know when trying to communicate via satellite is where the satellites are. One way to determine the location of a satellite at a given time is by using the Keplerian elements for the satellite. Keplerian elements are the parameters that define the orbit of a satellite, and they are widely available on the internet.

QUESTION: What are Keplerian elements? (E2A06)

ANSWER: **Parameters that define the orbit of a satellite**

Most amateur radio satellites are in a low Earth orbit, or LEO. What this means is that they are constantly changing position in relationship to a point on the Earth. So, to make contacts via a satellite, you have to track the path of the satellite as it travels through the sky.

Some satellites circle the earth from north to south, while others travel from south to north. When the satellite travels from north to south, we call that a descending pass; when the satellite travels from south to north, it's called an ascending pass. It's also important to know the direction in which it is traveling. The direction of an ascending pass for an amateur satellite is from south to north.

QUESTION: What is the direction of an ascending pass for

an amateur satellite? (E2A01)

ANSWER: **From south to north**

There is, however, now a geostationary satellite, the QO-100, that is available for amateur radio use. A geostationary satellite appears to stay in one position in the sky.

QUESTION: What type of satellite appears to stay in one position in the sky? (E2A10)

ANSWER: **Geostationary**

Another thing that you need to know to successfully make satellite contacts is the satellite's mode. The mode is a two-letter combination that tells you the satellite's uplink and downlink frequency bands. The first letter denotes the uplink frequency band; the second letter the downlink frequency band. U stands for UHF, V for VHF. So, if a satellite's mode is said to be U/V, then the uplink is in a UHF band and the downlink is in a VHF band.

QUESTION: What is meant by the term mode? as applied to an amateur radio satellite? (E2A04)

ANSWER: **The satellite's uplink and downlink frequency bands**

QUESTION: What do the letters in a satellite's mode designator specify? (E2A05)

ANSWER: **The uplink and downlink frequency ranges**

Some amateur satellites operate in the microwave bands, including the L band (23 cm) and S band (13 cm).

QUESTION: What do the terms L band and S band specify regarding satellite communications? (E2A09)

ANSWER: **The 23 centimeter and 13 centimeter bands**

Most FM satellites are simply FM repeaters in space. Some satellites, however, are more sophisticated. They repeat signals using linear transponders. Transponders are similar to repeaters, except that they receive signals of many different types, including FM, CW, SSB, SSTV, PSK, and packet signals, across a band of frequencies and repeat them across another band of frequencies.

In a satellite that uses an inverting linear transponder, an incoming signal is passed through a mixer, and the satellite transmits the difference rather than the sum. Inverting linear transponders reverse the signal position in the band and transform upper sideband signals on the uplink to lower sideband signals on the downlink and vice versa. Another consequence of using an inverting linear transponder is that Doppler shift is reduced because the uplink and downlink shifts are in the opposite directions.

QUESTION: Which of the following occurs when a satellite is using an inverting linear transponder? (E2A02)

ANSWER: **All these choices are correct**

- Doppler shift is reduced because the uplink and downlink shifts are in opposite directions

- Signal position in the band is reversed

- Upper sideband on the uplink becomes lower sideband on the downlink, and vice versa

QUESTION: How is the signal inverted by an inverting linear transponder? (E2A03)

ANSWER: **The signal is passed through a mixer and the difference rather than the sum is transmitted**

One thing to keep in mind when making contacts via a satellite using a linear transponder is to keep your transmitter power to the minimum needed to hit the satellite. The reason for this is that the transponder has a limited power output and the more power that your signal has reduces the downlink power available to other users.

QUESTION: Which of the following types of signals can be relayed through a linear transponder? (E2A07)

ANSWER: **All these choices are correct**

- FM and CW

- SSB and SSTV

- PSK and Packet

QUESTION: Why should effective radiated power to a satellite that uses a linear transponder be limited? (E2A08)

ANSWER: **To avoid reducing the downlink power to all other users**

Some low Earth orbiting satellites are capable of relaying messages around the world using a technique called store-and-forward. Satellites that use this technique store digital messages sent by one station for later download by another station that is not currently in the coverage area of the satellite.

QUESTION: Which of the following techniques is normally used by low Earth orbiting digital satellites to relay messages around the world? (E2A13)

ANSWER: **Store-and-forward**

QUESTION: What is the purpose of digital store-and-forward functions on an amateur radio satellite? (E2A12)

ANSWER: **To store digital messages in the satellite for later download by other stations**

There are quite a few interesting phenomena that result from the fact that satellites rotate while they are orbiting. For example, an amateur satellite may exhibit a rapidly repeating fading effect as the satellite's antenna rotates away from the receiving station and then towards the receiving staton. This is called spin fading or spin modulation. The polarization of a radio waves from a satellite also changes as it passes into the magnetic field of the Earth. This is called Faraday rotation. To minimize the effects of these two phenomena, most satellites use a circularly polarized antenna.

QUESTION: What type of antenna can be used to minimize

the effects of spin modulation and Faraday rotation? (E2A11)

ANSWER: **A circularly polarized antenna**

E2B - Television practices: fast scan television standards and techniques; slow scan television standards and techniques

Although we are called "radio" amateurs, we can also transmit and receive television signals. There are several ways that amateurs communicate by television. Two of the most popular ways send and receive television signals are standard fast-scan television and slow-scan television (SSTV).

The video standard used by North American fast-scan ATV stations was established by the National Television Systems Committee (NTSC) and was used for television systems in the U.S. and many other parts of the world. After nearly 70 years of using the analog NTSC system, U.S. broadcasters switched over to a digital broadcasting system on June 12, 2009.

A fast-scan (NTSC) television frame has 525 horizontal lines, and a new frame is transmitted 30 times per second in a fast-scan (NTSC) television system. NTSC systems use an interlaced scanning pattern. An interlaced scanning pattern is generated in a fast-scan (NTSC) television system by scanning odd numbered lines in one field and even numbered ones in the next.

Fast-scan television operation normally occurs on the 70 cm band. The reason for this is that the band is wide enough to accommodate the 6-MHz wide signal and commercial analog TV receivers can be used to receive the signals. The transmissions occur on channels shared with cable TV.

QUESTION: How many horizontal lines make up a fast-scan (NTSC) television frame? (E2B02)

ANSWER: **525**

QUESTION: How many times per second is a new frame transmitted in a fast-scan (NTSC) television system? (E2B01)

ANSWER: **30**

QUESTION: How is an interlaced scanning pattern generated in a fast-scan (NTSC) television system? (E2B03)

ANSWER: **By scanning odd numbered lines in one field and even numbered lines in the next**

QUESTION: What technique allows commercial analog TV

receivers to be used for fast-scan TV operations on the 70 cm band? (E2B08)

ANSWER: **Transmitting on channels shared with cable TV**

NTSC signals are amplitude modulated (AM) signals, but use a technique called vestigial sideband modulation. Vestigial sideband modulation is amplitude modulation in which one complete sideband and a portion of the other are transmitted. The reason that NTSC TV uses vestigial modulation is to conserve bandwidth. Even using this technique, an NTSC signal is 6 MHz wide. One advantage of using vestigial sideband for standard fast-scan TV transmissions is that vestigial sideband reduces bandwidth while allowing for simple video detector circuitry.

QUESTION: What is vestigial sideband modulation? (E2B06)

ANSWER: **Amplitude modulation in which one complete sideband and a portion of the other are transmitted**

QUESTION: Which of the following describes the use of vestigial sideband in analog fast-scan TV transmissions? (E2B05)

ANSWER: **Vestigial sideband reduces bandwidth while allowing for simple video detector circuitry**

Amateurs can transmit color TV as well as black-and-white TV. In a color TV signal, the color lines are sent sequentially. The name of the signal component that carries color information in NTSC video is chroma.

QUESTION: How is color information sent in analog SSTV? (E2B04)

ANSWER: **Color lines are sent sequentially**

QUESTION: What is the name of the signal component that carries color information in NTSC video? (E2B07)

ANSWER: **Chroma**

Slow-scan TV (SSTV)

SSTV images are typically transmitted on the HF bands using single sideband. Because of this, amateurs can only operate SSTV in the phone portions of the HF bands, and the bandwidth of the SSTV signal can be no greater than a normal SSB signal. The tone frequency of the single sideband signal determines the brightness of the picture, and specific tone frequencies signal SSTV receiving equipment to begin a new picture line.

QUESTION: What aspect of an analog slow-scan television signal encodes the brightness of the picture? (E2B10)

ANSWER: **Tone frequency**

QUESTION: What signals SSTV receiving software to begin a new picture line? (E2B12)

ANSWER: **Specific tone frequencies**

There are a number of different SSTV modes. The function of the Vertical Interval Signaling (VIS) code transmitted as part of an SSTV transmission is to identify the SSTV mode being used.

QUESTION: What is the function of the Vertical Interval Signaling (VIS) code sent as part of an SSTV transmission? (E2B11)

ANSWER: **To identify the SSTV mode being used**

Digital Radio Mondiale is one way to send and receive SSTV signals. **No other hardware is needed**, other than a receiver with SSB capability and a suitable computer, to decode SSTV using Digital Radio Mondiale (DRM).

QUESTION: What hardware, other than a receiver with SSB capability and a suitable computer, is needed to decode SSTV using Digital Radio Mondiale (DRM)? (E2B09)

ANSWER: **No other hardware is needed**

E2C – Operating methods: contest and DX operating; remote operation techniques; Cabrillo format; QSLing; RF network connected systems

Contesting is one of the most popular activities in amateur radio. While the rules differ from contest to contest, in general, the goal is to make as many contacts as possible in a given time period.

To enter a contest and be considered for awards, you must submit a log of your contacts. The contest organizers will check the log to make sure that you actually made the contacts that you claim. To make this easier to do, most contest organizers now request that you send in a digital file that lists your contacts in the Cabrillo format.

QUESTION: What is the Cabrillo format? (E2C07)

ANSWER: **A standard for submission of electronic contest logs**

There are some operating practices that are either prohibited or highly discouraged when operating a contest. On the HF bands, for example, operating on the "WARC bands," is normally prohibited. The "WARC bands" include 30 meters, 17 meters and 12 meters.

QUESTION: From which of the following bands is amateur radio contesting generally excluded? (E2C03)

ANSWER: **30 meters**

Another prohibited practice is "self-spotting," which is posting your own call sign and frequency on a call sign spotting network. The reason this is prohibited is that gives those that do it an advantage over other operators.

QUESTION: Which of the following best describes the term self-spotting? in connection with HF contest operating? (E2C02)

ANSWER: **The often-prohibited practice of posting one's own call sign and frequency on a spotting network**

VHF/UHF contests rarely include FM operation. During a VHF/UHF contest, you would, therefore, expect to find the highest level of activity in the weak signal segment of the band, with most of the activity near the calling frequency.

QUESTION: During a VHF/UHF contest, in which band segment would you expect to find the highest level of SSB or CW activity? (E2C06)

ANSWER: **In the weak signal segment of the band, with most of the activity near the calling frequency**

"Working" DX

"Working DX," or contacting stations in far-off places, is one of the most popular amateur radio activities. To be successful at working DX you need to know the protocol or etiquette involved in doing so. Because many stations may be calling a DX station working a pileup or a contest, send your call sign only once or twice and let the DX station pick you out of the pileup.

QUESTION: How should you generally identify your station when attempting to contact a DX station during a contest or in a pileup? (E2C11)

ANSWER: **Send your full call sign once or twice**

When many stations want to contact a DX station, it becomes almost impossible for the DX station to hear anyone calling him if they are all calling him on the frequency he's transmitting on. Instead, what usually happens is that the DX station will listen for calls on another frequency, usually above the frequency on which he is transmitting. We call this "split operation." Split operation separates the calling stations from the DX station and reduces interference, thereby improving operator efficiency. It also allows the DX station to transmit on a frequency that is prohibited to some responding stations, while allowing responding stations to call on frequencies on which they have privileges.

QUESTION: Why might a DX station state that they are listening on another frequency? (E2C10)

ANSWER: **All these choices are correct**

- Because the DX station may be transmitting on a frequency that is prohibited to some responding stations

- To separate the calling stations from the DX station

- To improve operating efficiency by reducing interference

QSLing

After you've made contact with a DX station, you may want to receive confirmation of that contact. You'll need confirmation, for example, to qualify for awards, such as Worked All Continents or the DX Century Club. An economical way to do this is to use the QSL bureau. Contacts between a U.S. station and a non-U.S. station may be confirmed through the U.S. QSL bureau system.

> QUESTION: Which of the following contacts may be confirmed through the U.S. QSL bureau system? (E2C08)
>
> ANSWER: **Contacts between a U.S. station and a non-U.S. station**

What the bureau does is group QSL cards to be sent to a particular country and sends hundreds or thousands of them in a single shipment to the QSL bureau in that country. The DX QSL bureau then sorts the cards and sends them to individual amateurs. This makes sending and receiving QSL cards from DX station much cheaper, but it may take a year or more to receive a reply from a DX station.

Some DX stations have QSL managers handle the sometimes arduous task of QSLing for them. The function of a DX QSL Manager is to handle the receiving and sending of confirmation cards for a DX station. The nice thing about sending QSL cards to and receiving QSL cards from a QSL manager is that the process is often much faster than going through a bureau.

> QUESTION: What is the function of a DX QSL Manager? (E2C05)
>
> ANSWER: **To handle the receiving and sending of confirmation cards for a DX station**

Mesh networks and remote operation

Because the amateur radio band at 2.4 GHZ overlaps with some WiFi channels, some amateurs are using those frequencies to set up digital networks called mesh networks. The cool thing about this is that you can use an off-the-shelf wireless router running custom firmware to set up a node on a mesh network. These nodes use discovery and link establishment protocols to form the network. Because amateur radio is a licensed service, and WiFi is an unlicensed service, amateur radio applications actually take priority over WiFi.

QUESTION: What type of equipment is commonly used to implement an amateur radio mesh network? (E2C09)

ANSWER: **A wireless router running custom firmware**

QUESTION: Which of the following frequencies are sometimes used for amateur radio mesh networks? (E2C04)

ANSWER: **Frequencies shared with various unlicensed wireless data services**

QUESTION: What technique do individual nodes use to form a mesh network? (E2C12)

ANSWER: **Discovery and link establishment protocols**

Connecting to amateur radio stations over the Internet has made remote operation easier than ever before. A frequently asked question about remote operation is whether or not a special indicator is required when operating a remote station. No additional indicator is required to be used by U.S.-licensed operators when operating a station via remote control where the transmitter is located in the U.S.

QUESTION: What indicator is required to be used by U.S.-licensed operators when operating a station via remote control and the remote transmitter is located in the U.S.? (E2C01)

ANSWER: **No additional indicator is required**

E2D – Operating methods: VHF and UHF digital modes and procedures; APRS; EME procedures, meteor scatter procedures

In the past ten years or so, the number of digital modes has just exploded. JT65 is one example. The type of modulation used for JT65 contacts is multi-tone AFSK. One advantage of using JT65 coding is the ability to decode signals which have a very low signal to noise ratio.

JT65 is a digital mode especially useful for EME communications. One of the reasons that JT65 is such an effective method of establishing EME contacts is because it uses time synchronous transmissions alternately from each station.

QUESTION: What type of modulation is used for JT65 contacts? (E2D09)

ANSWER: **Multi-tone AFSK**

QUESTION: What is one advantage of the JT65 mode? (E2D05)

ANSWER: **The ability to decode signals which have a very low signal-to-noise ratio**

QUESTION: Which of the following digital modes is especially useful for EME communications? (E2D03)

ANSWER: **JT65**

QUESTION: Which of the following describes a method of establishing EME contacts? (E2D06)

ANSWER: **Time synchronous transmissions alternately from each station**

APRS

One of the most popular digital modes is the Automatic Packet Reporting System, or APRS. Most APRS operation takes place on the 2 m band around 144.39 MHz.

AX.25 is the digital protocol used by APRS. AX.25 is more commonly known as packet radio. Stations transmit APRS beacon data using unnumbered information packet frames.

APRS stations are often used to help support a public service communications activity. An APRS station with a GPS unit can automatically transmit information to show a mobile station's position during the event. Latitude and longitude are used by the APRS network to communicate your location.

APRS is also used to track high-altitude balloons. The teams monitor the APRS transmissions to determine the altitude that the balloon reaches and to locate the payload once the balloon bursts and the payload falls to Earth.

QUESTION: What digital protocol is used by APRS? (E2D07)

ANSWER: **AX.25**

QUESTION: What type of packet frame is used to transmit APRS beacon data? (E2D08)

ANSWER: **Unnumbered Information**

QUESTION: How can an APRS station be used to help support a public service communications activity? (E2D10)

ANSWER: **An APRS station with a Global Positioning System unit can automatically transmit information to show a mobile station's position during the event**

QUESTION: Which of the following data are used by the APRS network to communicate station location? (E2D11)

ANSWER: **Latitude and longitude**

QUESTION: What technology is used to track, in real time, balloons carrying amateur radio transmitters? (E2D04)

ANSWER: **APRS**

Meteor scatter

Digital modes can also be used to make meteor scatter contacts. MSK144 is a digital mode especially designed for use for meteor scatter signals. Good techniques for making meteor scatter contacts include 15-second timed transmission sequences with stations alternating based on location, use of special digital modes, and short transmissions with rapidly repeated call signs and signal reports.

QUESTION: Which of the following digital modes is designed for meteor scatter communications? (E2D01)

ANSWER: **MSK144**

QUESTION: Which of the following is a good technique for making meteor scatter contacts? (E2D02)

ANSWER: **All these choices are correct**

- 15-second timed transmission sequences with stations alternating based on location

- Use of special digital modes

- Short transmissions with rapidly repeated call signs and signal reports

E2E – Operating methods: operating HF digital modes

Although many digital mode operators have switched to FT8, PSK31 remains a popular digital mode. PSK stands for "phase shift keying." One of its main advantages is that it had a very narrow bandwidth—only 31 Hz. One of the reasons that PSK31 has such a narrow bandwidth is that it uses variable length coding. That is to say, characters have different numbers of bits, depending on how frequently they appear in normal text.

QUESTION: Which of these digital modes has the narrowest bandwidth? (E2E10)

ANSWER: **PSK31**

QUESTION: Which of the following HF digital modes uses variable-length coding for bandwidth efficiency? (E2E09)

ANSWER: **PSK31**

Another type of modulation commonly used on the HF bands is frequency-shift keying, or FSK. FSK is a type of modulation that is common for data emissions below 30 MHz. RTTY, for example uses FSK modulation. It shifts between two different frequencies, which denote "mark" and "space," which then translate to one and zero.

Amateur transceivers use two different methods to modulate a signal using FSK: direct FSK and audio FSK. In direct FSK, a digital signal is connected to the transceiver to shift the frequency. When using audio FSK, the transceiver is set up to transmit an SSB signal and an audio signal, typically from a computer sound card, is used to shift the frequency of the transmitted signal. The biggest difference between the two methods is that when using direct FSK, the FSK signal occupies less bandwidth.

QUESTION: Which of the following types of modulation is common for data emissions below 30 MHz? (E2E01)

ANSWER: **FSK**

QUESTION: What is the difference between direct FSK and audio FSK? (E2E11)

ANSWER: **Direct FSK occupies less bandwidth**

To tune an FSK signal, one often uses a crossed-ellipse display. You have properly tuned a signal when one of the ellipses is as vertical as possible, and the other is as horizontal as possible. When one of the ellipses in an FSK crossed-ellipse display suddenly disappears, selective fading has occurred.

QUESTION: What is indicated when one of the ellipses in an FSK crossed-ellipse display suddenly disappears? (E2E04)

ANSWER: **Selective fading has occurred**

PACTOR is another digital mode that uses FSK. It uses the ARQ protocol to detect errors, and because of this, you can use PACTOR to transfer binary files error-free. One of the disadvantages of PACTOR is that you can't use it for keyboard-keyboard communications like you can RTTY and PSK31.

QUESTION: Which of the following HF digital modes can be used to transfer binary files? (E2E08)

ANSWER: **PACTOR**

QUESTION: Which of these digital modes does not support keyboard-to-keyboard operation? (E2E05)

ANSWER: **PACTOR**

Another way to detect and correct errors in a data transmission is forward error correction (FEC). Digital transmission systems that use forward error correction send redundant data that not only allows a receiver to detect errors, but also correct some errors.

QUESTION: What do the letters FEC mean as they relate to digital operation? (E2E02)

ANSWER: **Forward Error Correction**

No matter what type of modulation you use, data transmission over an HF radio link is very slow. 300 baud is the most common data rate used for HF packet communications. In fact, due to bandwidth limitations, 300 baud is the maximum symbol rate. Under clear communication conditions, 300 baud packet has the fastest data throughput on the HF bands.

QUESTION: What is the most common data rate used for HF packet? (E2E06)

ANSWER: **300 baud**

QUESTION: Which of these digital modes has the fastest data throughput under clear communication conditions? (E2E13)

ANSWER: **300 baud packet**

Some HF digital modes operate automatically, that is to say the software running these digital modes automatically initiate and maintain the connection. One technique for doing this is called Automatic Link Enable (ALE). ALE stations establish contact by constantly scanning a list of frequencies, then activating a radio when it receives a designated call sign. There are many reasons that you may not be able to initiate a contact with an ALE or other digital station, including using the wrong transmit frequency, using a protocol not supported by the digital station, or another station, that you may not be able to hear, is using the frequency.

QUESTION: How do ALE stations establish contact? (E2E12)

ANSWER: **ALE constantly scans a list of frequencies, activating the radio when the designated call sign is received**

QUESTION: Which of the following is a possible reason that attempts to initiate contact with a digital station on a clear frequency are unsuccessful? (E2E07)

ANSWER: **All these choices are correct**

- Your transmit frequency is incorrect

- The protocol version you are using is not supported by the digital station

- Another station you are unable to hear is using the frequency

One digital mode that is becoming quite popular is FT4. Part of the WSJT suite, it is similar to FT8 in that it uses fixed-length transmissions, structured messages with formats optimized for minimal QSOs, and strong forward error correction. The biggest difference is that FT4 has a 7.5 s transmit/receive cycle instead of a 15 s cycle. The tradeoff is that FT4's weak-signal performance is not quite as good as the weak signal performance of FT8.

QUESTION: How is the timing of FT4 contacts organized? (E2E03)

ANSWER: **Alternating transmissions at 7.5 second intervals**

E0: SAFETY

E0A Safety: RF radiation hazards; hazardous materials; grounding

No matter what amateur radio activities you engage in, I hope that you will engage in them safely. Every year, we lose amateur radio operators because of injuries they sustained while putting up antennas or doing things that could be dangerous. We don't want to lose you.

Perhaps the most common danger is from lightning strikes. To protect your station, use an external earth connection or ground rod.

QUESTION: What is the primary function of an external earth connection or ground rod? (E0A01)

ANSWER: **Lightning protection**

RF exposure is another hazard. One of the ways that RF exposure can be hazardous is by causing human tissue to heat up. The amount of heating is proportional to the specific absorption rate (SAR), which is the rate at which RF energy is absorbed by the body.

QUESTION: What does SAR measure? (E0A08)

ANSWER: **The rate at which RF energy is absorbed by the body**

In order to prevent injuries from RF exposure, the FCC has set maximum permissible exposure (MPE) limits. An MPE limit is the level at which harmful biological effects can occur. Several organizations, including the National Council on Radiation Protection and Measurements (NCRP) and the Institute of Electrical and Electronics Engineers (IEEE) have provided the data used by the FCC to set MPEs. RF exposure limits are most restrictive between 30 and 300 MHz because the human body absorbs radiation at those frequencies more than others.

QUESTION: Over what range of frequencies are the FCC human body RF exposure limits most restrictive? (E0A03)

ANSWER: **30 to 300 MHz**

Amateurs operating the microwave bands must also be careful. After all, think about how a microwave oven works. High-power UHF or microwave radiation can also heat up body tissue. Excessive RF exposure can also result from using high-gain antennas when operating the microwave bands.

QUESTION: Which of the following injuries can result from using high-power UHF or microwave transmitters? (E0A11)

ANSWER: **Localized heating of the body from RF exposure in excess of the MPE limits**

QUESTION: What is one of the potential hazards of operating in the amateur radio microwave bands? (E0A05)

ANSWER: **The high gain antennas commonly used can result in high exposure levels**

MPE limits for the electric field and magnetic field of an electromagnetic wave differ. There are several reasons for this. First, the body reacts to electromagnetic radiation from both the E and H fields. Second, ground reflections and scattering make the field impedance vary with location. Third, E field and H field radiation intensity peaks can occur at different locations.

QUESTION: Why are there separate electric (E) and magnetic (H) field MPE limits? (E0A06)

ANSWER: **All these choices are correct**

- The body reacts to electromagnetic radiation from both the E and H fields

- Ground reflections and scattering make the field strength vary with location

- E field and H field radiation intensity peaks can occur at different locations

Remember to include your neighbors when evaluating RF exposure levels. In some cases, your antennas may actually be closer to your neighbors' houses than they are to your house. That's why FCC rules require that you must make sure signals from your station are less than the uncontrolled MPE limits when evaluating RF exposure levels from your station at a neighbor's home.

QUESTION: When evaluating RF exposure levels from your station at a neighbor's home, what must you do? (E0A02)

ANSWER: **Ensure signals from your station are less than the uncontrolled Maximum Permitted Exposure (MPE) limits**

Typically, amateur repeater stations are located in places where there are transmitters for other radio services, such as cell phone and pager services. These sites should be regularly evaluated so that RF field strengths don't exceed the MPE limits. When evaluating a site with multiple transmitters operating at the same time, the operators and licensees of each transmitter that produces 5 percent or more of its MPE exposure limit at accessible locations are responsible for mitigating over-exposure situations.

QUESTION: When evaluating a site with multiple transmitters operating at the same time, the operators and licensees of which transmitters are responsible for mitigating over-exposure situations? (E0A04)

ANSWER: **Each transmitter that produces 5 percent or more of its MPE limit in areas where the total MPE limit is**

exceeded

Lightning and RF exposure are not the only dangers posed by an amateur radio station. For example, in emergency situations, you may want to use a gasoline-powered generator. One of the dangers posed by a gas-powered generator is that its exhaust contains carbon monoxide. To ensure your safety and those around you, make sure you use a carbon monoxide detector wherever fumes may accumulate.

How may dangerous levels of carbon monoxide from an emergency generator be detected? (E0A07)

ANSWER: **Only with a carbon monoxide detector**

Some of the materials used in electronics pose a danger to amateur radio operators. They are used because they have some desirable electrical property, but may be dangerous if used improperly. For example, beryllium oxide is an insulating material commonly used as a thermal conductor for some types of electronic devices that is extremely toxic if broken or crushed and the particles are accidentally inhaled. Another toxic material, polychlorinated biphenyls (PCBs), can be found in some electronic components, such as high-voltage capacitors and transformers.

QUESTION: Which insulating material commonly used as a thermal conductor for some types of electronic devices is extremely toxic if broken or crushed and the particles are accidentally inhaled? (E0A09)

ANSWER: **Beryllium Oxide**

QUESTION: What toxic material may be present in some electronic components such as high voltage capacitors and transformers? (E0A10)

ANSWER: **Polychlorinated biphenyls**

E1: COMMISSION'S RULES

E1A Operating Standards: frequency privileges; automatic message forwarding; stations aboard ships or aircraft; power restriction on 630 and 2200 meter bands

One of the most important things you must do when operating an amateur radio station is to make sure that your signal stays within the amateur radio band or sub-band. So, for example, you don't want to operate at the very bottom of the phone band, if operating phone, or at the very bottom of the CW/data portion of a band if your operating LSB AFSK. Nor do you want to operate at the upper end of the CW/data portion of the band if you're operating USB AFSK. The reason for this is that your signals will illegally extend outside the band or portion of the band where you have operating privileges.

QUESTION: Which of the following carrier frequencies is illegal for LSB AFSK emissions on the 17 meter band RTTY and data segment of 18.068 to 18.110 MHz? (E1A01)

ANSWER: **18.068 MHz**

If you set your carrier frequency to 18.068 MHz, your signal will extend beyond the bottom of the 17-meter band.

QUESTION: What is the maximum legal carrier frequency on the 20 meter band for transmitting USB AFSK digital signals having a 1 kHz bandwidth? (E1A03)

ANSWER: **14.149 MHz**

If you set your carrier frequency to 14.149 MHz, your signal could potentially extend beyond 14.150 MHz, which is the upper limit of CW/data segment of the 20-meter band.

This may also happen if you operate phone. When operating phone using LSB on 40m or 80m, you must set your transmitter carrier frequency to at least 3 kHz above the lower band edge to ensure that your signal does not extend into the CW/data portion of the band. For example, if you hear a DX station calling CQ on 3.601 MHz LSB, it would be illegal to return that call using LSB on that same frequency because your signal will extend beyond the lower edge of the phone band (3.598 – 3.601 MHz).

QUESTION: When using a transceiver that displays the carrier frequency of phone signals, which of the following displayed frequencies represents the lowest frequency at which a properly adjusted LSB emission will be totally within the band? (E1A02)

ANSWER: **3 kHz above the lower band edge**

QUESTION: With your transceiver displaying the carrier frequency of phone signals, you hear a DX station calling CQ on 3.601 MHz LSB. Is it legal to return the call using lower sideband on the same frequency? (E1A04)

ANSWER: **No, the sideband will extend beyond the edge of the phone band segment**

Similarly, you must make sure that your SSTV signals stay within the phone segments of the band on which you're operating. So, make sure not to set your carrier frequency too low if operating LSB or too high if operating USB.

QUESTION: What special operating frequency restrictions are imposed on slow scan TV transmissions? (E1A12)

ANSWER: **They are restricted to phone band segments**

60 meter, 630 meter and 2200 meter bands

The 60 m band is one of the oddest amateur radio bands. One of the reasons for this is that the 60 meter band is the only amateur band where transmission on specific channels rather than a range of frequencies is permitted. Practically, what this means is that the carrier frequency of a CW signal must be set at the center frequency of the channel.

The rules for power output are also a bit arcane. The maximum power output permitted on the 60 meter band is 100 watts PEP effective radiated power relative to the gain of a half-wave dipole. The rules are written this way to minimize interference between amateur radio operators, who are secondary users of this band, and the primary users, which are primarily government radio stations.

There are also power output limitations on the relatively new 630 meter and 2200 meter bands. The power limits are 1 watt and 5 watts, respectively.

QUESTION: Where must the carrier frequency of a CW signal be set to comply with FCC rules for 60 meter operation? (E1A06)

ANSWER: **At the center frequency of the channel**

QUESTION: What is the maximum power output permitted on the 60 meter band? (E1A05)

ANSWER: **100 watts PEP effective radiated power relative to the gain of a half-wave dipole**

QUESTION: What is the maximum power permitted on the 2200 meter band? (E1A07)

ANSWER: **1 watt EIRP (Equivalent isotropic radiated power)**

QUESTION: Except in some parts of Alaska, what is the maximum power permitted on the 630 meter band? (E1A14)

ANSWER: **5 watts EIRP**

Winlink

Some amateur radio systems automatically forward messages for other amateur radio stations. Winlink is one such system. There is always a question of who is responsible when an automatically-controlled station forwards a message that violates FCC rules. If a station in a message forwarding system inadvertently forwards a message that is in violation of FCC rules, the control operator of the originating station is primarily accountable for the rules violation. This is very similar to the situation where a repeater is used to send messages that violate FCC rules.

> QUESTION: If a station in a message forwarding system inadvertently forwards a message that is in violation of FCC rules, who is primarily accountable for the rules violation? (E1A08)
>
> ANSWER: **The control operator of the originating station**

The first action you should take if your digital message forwarding station inadvertently forwards a communication that violates FCC rules is to discontinue forwarding the communication as soon as you become aware of it. This is also similar to what a repeater control operator should do if a repeater user is violating FCC rules.

> QUESTION: What action or actions should you take if your digital message forwarding station inadvertently forwards a communication that violates FCC rules? (E1A09)
>
> ANSWER: **Discontinue forwarding the communication as soon as you become aware of it**

Operating aboard a ship or airplane

Operating an amateur radio station aboard a ship or an airplane can be a lot of fun, but there are rules that govern this operation. First of all, you need an FCC-issued amateur license to operate an amateur station aboard a U.S.-registered vessel in international waters. Also, before operating an amateur station installed aboard a ship or aircraft, you must get the approval of the master of the ship or the pilot of the aircraft.

> QUESTION: Which of the following describes authorization or licensing required when operating an amateur station aboard a U.S.-registered vessel in international waters? (E1A11)
>
> ANSWER: **Any FCC-issued amateur license**

> QUESTION: If an amateur station is installed aboard a ship

or aircraft, what condition must be met before the station is operated? (E1A10)

ANSWER: **Its operation must be approved by the master of the ship or the pilot in command of the aircraft**

Even when operating from a ship, there must be a control operator. Someone holding an FCC-issued amateur license or who is authorized for alien reciprocal operation must be in physical control of the station.

QUESTION: Who must be in physical control of the station apparatus of an amateur station aboard any vessel or craft that is documented or registered in the United States? (E1A13)

ANSWER: **Any person holding an FCC issued amateur license or who is authorized for alien reciprocal operation**

E1B – Station restrictions and special operations: restrictions on station location; general operating restrictions; spurious emissions; antenna structure restrictions; RACES operations

Part 97 places many different restrictions on how amateurs can use their stations and specifies technical standards that amateur radio station must meet. For example, some rules set standards for spurious emissions, which are emissions outside a signal's necessary bandwidth that can be reduced or eliminated without affecting the information transmitted.

> QUESTION: Which of the following constitutes a spurious emission? (E1B01)

> ANSWER: **An emission outside the signal's necessary bandwidth that can be reduced or eliminated without affecting the information transmitted**

There are also restrictions on erecting antennas. For example, if you are installing an amateur station antenna at a site at or near a public use airport, you may have to notify the Federal Aviation Administration and register it with the FCC as required by Part 17 of FCC rules.

> QUESTION: Which of the following additional rules apply if you are installing an amateur station antenna at a site at or near a public use airport? (E1B06)

> ANSWER: **You may have to notify the Federal Aviation Administration and register it with the FCC as required by Part 17 of the FCC rules**

Should you run into problems with your local government when erecting an antenna, you should familiarize yourself with FCC PRB-1. PRB-1 states that while local governments may put restrictions on antenna structures for height, safety and aesthetics concerns, they must reasonably accommodate amateur operations. It is important to note that PRB-1 does not cover covenants or home-owner agreements (HOAs).

> QUESTION: To what type of regulations does PRB-1 apply? (E1B07)

ANSWER: **State and local zoning**

QUESTION: What does PRB-1 require of regulations affecting amateur radio? (E1B11)

ANSWER: **Reasonable accommodations of amateur radio must be made**

RACES operation

The Radio Amateur Civil Emergency Service (RACES) is a quasi-governmental organization managed by the Federal Emergency Management Agency (FEMA) and governed by Part 97 rules. Any FCC-licensed amateur station certified by the responsible civil defense organization for the area served may be operated under RACES rules, and all amateur service frequencies authorized to the control operator are authorized to an amateur station participating in RACES.

QUESTION: Which amateur stations may be operated under RACES rules? (E1B09)

ANSWER: **Any FCC-licensed amateur station certified by the responsible civil defense organization for the area served**

QUESTION: What frequencies are authorized to an amateur station operating under RACES rules? (E1B10)

ANSWER: **All amateur service frequencies authorized to the control operator**

As you probably know by now, harmful interference is a big thing in amateur radio. That being the case, this section has several questions about situations in which an amateur station might cause such interference.

QUESTION: Within what distance must an amateur station protect an FCC monitoring facility from harmful interference? (E1B03)

ANSWER: **1 mile**

QUESTION: What must be done before placing an amateur station within an officially designated wilderness area or wildlife preserve, or an area listed in the National Register of Historic Places? (E1B04)

ANSWER: **An Environmental Assessment must be submitted to the FCC**

QUESTION: What is the National Radio Quiet Zone? (E1B05)

ANSWER: **An area surrounding the National Radio Astronomy Observatory**

The NRAO is located in Green Bank, West Virginia.

QUESTION: What limitations may the FCC place on an amateur station if its signal causes interference to domestic broadcast reception, assuming that the receivers involved are of good engineering design? (E1B08)

ANSWER: **The amateur station must avoid transmitting during certain hours on frequencies that cause the interference**

QUESTION: What must the control operator of a repeater operating in the 70 cm band do if a radiolocation system experiences interference from that repeater? (E1B12)

ANSWER: **Cease operation or make changes to the repeater to mitigate the interference**

Finally, there is a random question on Digital Radio Mondiale (DRM).

QUESTION: Which of the following is an acceptable bandwidth for Digital Radio Mondiale (DRM) based voice or SSTV digital transmissions made on the HF amateur bands? (E1B02)

ANSWER: **3 kHz**

E1C – Rules pertaining to automatic and remote control; band-specific regulations; operating in, and communicating with foreign countries; spurious emission standards; HF modulation index limit; bandwidth definition

An important concept in the rules governing amateur radio is the concept of station control and the control operator. The control operator is the licensed radio amateur who is responsible for the transmissions of a station, and the location of that operator is called the control point. There are three ways that a control operator can control a station: local control, remote control, or automatic control.

When the control operator is present at the station he or she is controlling, we say that the station is under local control. Control operators do not, however, have to be physically present at the station they are controlling. They can control a station via a radio link or via the internet, for example. If that link malfunctions, however, a remotely-controlled station may only transmit for up to 3 minutes.

QUESTION: How do the control operator responsibilities of a station under automatic control differ from one under local control? (E1C03)

ANSWER: **Under automatic control the control operator is not required to be present at the control point**

QUESTION: What is the maximum permissible duration of a remotely controlled station's transmissions if its control link malfunctions? (E1C08)

ANSWER: **3 minutes**

When a station is being automatically controlled, the control operator need not be at the control point. Repeater stations, for example, are usually automatically controlled, and the control operator is normally not at the control point. One thing to keep in mind is that an automatically controlled station may never originate third party communications.

QUESTION: When may an automatically controlled station

originate third party communications? (E1C05)

ANSWER: **Never**

IARP and CEPT licenses, third-party traffic

To operate in certain countries of the Americas, U.S. amateurs can apply for an International Amateur Radio Permit (IARP). Countries that accept an IARP include Argentina, Brazil, Canada, El Salvador, Panama, Paraguay, Peru, Trinidad and Tobago, United States of America, Uruguay, and Venezuela. In the U.S., IARPs are issued by the ARRL.

QUESTION: What is meant by IARP? (E1C04)

ANSWER: **An international amateur radio permit that allows U.S. amateurs to operate in certain countries of the Americas**

The CEPT agreement allows an FCC-licensed U.S. citizen to operate in many European countries, and alien amateurs from many European countries to operate in the U.S. There are 40 European countries that allow you to operate under the CEPT agreement. If you do plan to operate in a foreign country under the CEPT agreement, make sure to obtain and bring with you a copy of FCC Public Notice DA 16-048.

QUESTION: Which of the following operating arrangements allows an FCC-licensed U.S. citizen to operate in many European countries, and alien amateurs from many European countries to operate in the U.S.? (E1C11)

ANSWER: **CEPT agreement**

QUESTION: Which of the following is required in order to operate in accordance with CEPT rules in foreign countries where permitted? (E1C06)

ANSWER: **You must bring a copy of FCC Public Notice DA 16-1048**

Although not a licensing issue, §97.117 notes, "Transmissions to a different country, where permitted, shall be limited to communications incidental to the purposes of the amateur service and to remarks of a personal character."

QUESTION: Which of the following types of communications may be transmitted to amateur stations in foreign countries? (E1C02)

ANSWER: **Communications incidental to the purpose of the amateur service and remarks of a personal nature**

Bandwidth and other technical requirements

Part 97 contains a number of rules relating to technical requirements that amateur radio stations must adhere to. For example, the maximum bandwidth for a data emission on the 60-meter band is 2.8 kHz, the same as a SSB phone emission. According to §97.3(a)(8), the bandwidth of a signal is, "The width of a frequency band outside of which the mean power of the transmitted signal is attenuated at least 26 dB below the mean power of the transmitted signal within the band."

QUESTION: What is the maximum bandwidth for a data emission on 60 meters? (E1C01)

ANSWER: **2.8 kHz**

QUESTION: At what level below a signal's mean power level is its bandwidth determined according to FCC rules? (E1C07)

ANSWER: **26 dB**

There is also a regulation that specifies allowable levels of spurious emissions from an amateur radio transmitter. §97.307(d) states, "For transmitters installed after January 1, 2003, the mean power of any spurious emission from a station transmitter or external RF power amplifier transmitting on a frequency below 30 MHz must be at least 43 dB below the mean power of the fundamental emission." Transmitters installed before January 1, 2003 have more lenient requirements.

QUESTION: What is the permitted mean power of any spurious emission relative to the mean power of the fundamental emission from a station transmitter or external RF amplifier installed after January 1, 2003 and transmitting on a frequency below 30 MHz? (E1C10)

ANSWER: **At least 43 dB below**

And a random question about modulation index on the 10 meter band.

QUESTION: What is the highest modulation index permitted at the highest modulation frequency for angle modulation below 29.0 MHz? (E1C09)

ANSWER: **1.0**

630 meter and 2200 meter band regulations

The International Telecommunications Union (ITU) allocated the 630 meter band (472 – 479 kHz) to amateur radio operators at the 2012 World Radiocommunications Conference (WRC-12). Although phone operation is permitted across the entire band, you must first notify the Utilities Technology Council (UTC) of your plans to do so. The reason for this is that in some areas of the country, power utilities use those frequencies to transmit data over the power lines, and they want to avoid any interference between amateurs and the utilities.

QUESTION: On what portion of the 630 meter band are phone emissions permitted? (E1C12)

ANSWER: **The entire band**

QUESTION: What notifications must be given before transmitting on the 630 meter or 2200 meter bands? (E1C13)

ANSWER: **Operators must inform the Utilities Technology Council (UTC) of their call sign and coordinates of the station**

QUESTION: How long must an operator wait after filing a notification with the Utilities Technology Council (UTC) before operating on the 2200 meter or 630 meter band? (E1C14)

ANSWER: **Operators may operate after 30 days, providing they have not been told that their station is within 1 km of PLC systems using those frequencies**

E1D – Amateur space and Earth stations; telemetry and telecommand rules; identification of balloon transmissions; one-way communications

One of the cool things that amateur radio operators can do is to use satellites to communicate with one anther. In the amateur satellite service, the satellites are called space stations and are remotely controlled by telecommands. Space stations can transmit on the 40m, 20m, 17m, 15m, 12m and 10m HF bands, the 2 meter VHF band, and the 70 cm and 13 cm UHF bands.

QUESTION: Which HF amateur bands have frequencies authorized for space stations? (E1D07)

ANSWER: **Only the 40, 20, 17, 15, 12, and 10 meter bands**

QUESTION: Which VHF amateur bands have frequencies authorized for space stations? (E1D08)

ANSWER: **2 meters**

QUESTION: Which UHF amateur bands have frequencies authorized for space stations? (E1D09)

ANSWER: **70 cm and 13 cm**

Space stations are controlled by telecommand stations, which are amateur stations that transmits communications to initiate, modify or terminate functions of a space station. Any amateur station designated by the space station licensee is eligible to be a telecommand station, assuming that the station's control operator has the appropriate privileges. In order to prevent malicious telecommands being sent to a space station, space telecommand stations may transmits special codes intended to obscure the meaning of a message. The only time amateur radio operators are allowed to use this type of encryption is when sending telecommands to a space station or a radio-controlled mode.

QUESTION: What is a space telecommand station? (E1D03)

ANSWER: **An amateur station that transmits communications to initiate, modify or terminate functions**

of a space station

QUESTION: Which amateur stations are eligible to be telecommand stations of space stations (subject to the privileges of the class of operator license held by the control operator of the station)? (E1D10)

ANSWER: **Any amateur station so designated by the space station licensee**

QUESTION: Which of the following may transmit special codes intended to obscure the meaning of messages? (E1D02)

ANSWER: **Telecommand signals from a space telecommand station**

To obtain information about the operation of a space station or a high-altitude balloon, the space station or balloon might send telemetry. Telemetry is the one-way transmission of measurements at a distance from the measuring instrument. For example, a space station might use telemetry to send information such as ambient temperature and battery status. In addition to the measurement information, the station sending telemetry must also identify with their call sign.

QUESTION: What is the definition of telemetry? (E1D01)

ANSWER: **One-way transmission of measurements at a distance from the measuring instrument**

QUESTION: Which of the following is required in the identification transmissions from a balloon-borne telemetry station? (E1D04)

ANSWER: **Call sign**

Telemetry is an example of a one-way communication, and one of very few cases in which amateur radio stations my transmit one-way communications. Space stations, beacon stations, and telecommand stations can all transmit one-way communications.

QUESTION: Which of the following amateur stations may transmit one-way communications? (E1D12)

ANSWER: **A space station, beacon station, or telecommand station**

Space stations operate at an altitude of 50 km or higher. Stations that operate below that altitude are called Earth stations. Any amateur station whose control operator has the appropriate privileges can operate as an Earth station,

QUESTION: Which amateur stations are eligible to operate as Earth stations? (E1D11)

ANSWER: **Any amateur station, subject to the privileges of the class of operator license held by the control operator**

Radio-controlled models

Amateur radio operators can use amateur radio frequencies to control model crafts. Instead of identifying on the air, a photocopy of the station license, a label with the name, address, and telephone number of the station licensee, and a label with the name, address, and telephone number of the control operator must be posted at the telecommand station location. A transmitter sending telecommands is limited to only 1 watt of output power.

QUESTION: What must be posted at the station location of a station being operated by telecommand on or within 50 km of the earth's surface? (E1D05)

ANSWER: **All these choices are correct**

- A photocopy of the station license

- A label with the name, address, and telephone number of the station licensee

- A label with the name, address, and telephone number of the control operator

QUESTION: What is the maximum permitted transmitter output power when operating a model craft by telecommand? (E1D06)

ANSWER: **1 watt**

E1E – Volunteer examiner program: definitions; qualifications; preparation and administration of exams; accreditation; question pools; documentation requirements

The Volunteer Examiner program started in the early 1980s, and has been a boon for amateur radio. Exam sessions are now more accessible than when tests were given by the FCC, meaning that it is much easier to obtain an amateur radio license, and that more people can now enjoy our hobby.

Volunteer Examiner Coordinators (VECs) are the organizations that have entered into an agreement with the FCC to coordinate amateur operator license examinations. There are currently 14 VECs in the U.S. Part 97 assigns VECs the task of maintaining the question pools used for U.S. amateur license examinations. VECs also accredit individual Volunteer Examiners (VEs). That is to say that they confirm that a VE applicant meets FCC requirements to serve as an examiner.

QUESTION: What is a Volunteer Examiner Coordinator? (E1E03)

ANSWER: **An organization that has entered into an agreement with the FCC to coordinate, prepare, and administer amateur operator license examinations**

QUESTION: Which of the following best describes the Volunteer Examiner accreditation process? (E1E04)

ANSWER: **The procedure by which a VEC confirms that the VE applicant meets FCC requirements to serve as an examiner**

QUESTION: Who does Part 97 task with maintaining the pools of questions for all U.S. amateur license examinations? (E1E02)

ANSWER: **The VECs**

As the name implies, volunteer examiners (VEs) are volunteers. They may not accept any payment for administering tests, but Part 97 rules state that VEs (and VECs) may be reimbursed for some out-of-pocket expenses, such as preparing, processing, administering and coordinating amateur radio license examinations.

QUESTION: For which types of out-of-pocket expenses do the Part 97 rules state that VEs and VECs may be reimbursed? (E1E01)

ANSWER: **Preparing, processing, administering, and coordinating an examination for an amateur radio operator license**

The rules and procedures for administering the tests are written so that everything is on the up and up. For example, each administering VE is responsible for the proper conduct and necessary supervision during an amateur operator license examination session. Having three VEs present at a test session, and making them all responsible for how they conduct the test session, leaves very little room for cheating.

VEs are not to show any favoritism. To minimize the chance of this happening, the FCC rules list relatives to whom a VE may not administer an examination. The penalty for a VE who fraudulently administers or certifies an examination can be revocation of the VE's amateur station license grant and the suspension of the VE's amateur operator license grant.

Before administering a test, the VEs instruct the candidates of the rules. For example, the candidates are not allowed to consult any books during the test. They may use a calculator, but only if they can demonstrate to a VE that all of the calculator's memories have been cleared. If a candidate fails to comply with the examiner's instructions during an amateur operator license examination, a VE must immediately terminate the candidate's examination.

QUESTION: Who is responsible for the proper conduct and necessary supervision during an amateur operator license examination session? (E1E06)

ANSWER: **Each administering VE**

QUESTION: To which of the following examinees may a VE not administer an examination? (E1E08)

ANSWER: **Relatives of the VE as listed in the FCC rules**

QUESTION: What may be the penalty for a VE who fraudulently administers or certifies an examination? (E1E09)

ANSWER: **Revocation of the VE's amateur station license grant and the suspension of the VE's amateur operator license grant**

QUESTION: What should a VE do if a candidate fails to comply with the examiner's instructions during an amateur operator license examination? (E1E07)

ANSWER: **Immediately terminate the candidate's examination**

Upon completion of an exam, three VEs must correct each test sheet. This minimizes the chance for making a scoring mistake. To pass the test, an examinee must achieve a minimum passing score of 74%. If an examinee scores a passing grade on all examination elements needed for an upgrade or new license, the three VEs must certify that the examinee is qualified for the license grant and that they have complied with the administering VE requirements.

After someone has successfully completed an examination for an amateur operator license, the VEs must submit the application document to the coordinating VEC according to the coordinating VEC instructions. If the examinee does not pass the exam, however, the VE team must return the application document to the examinee.

QUESTION: What is the minimum passing score on all amateur operator license examinations? (E1E05)

ANSWER: **Minimum passing score of 74%**

QUESTION: What must the VE team do if an examinee scores a passing grade on all examination elements needed for an upgrade or new license? (E1E11)

ANSWER: **Three VEs must certify that the examinee is qualified for the license grant and that they have complied with the administering VE requirements**

QUESTION: What must the administering VEs do after the administration of a successful examination for an amateur operator license? (E1E10)

ANSWER: **They must submit the application document to the coordinating VEC according to the coordinating VEC instructions**

QUESTION: What must the VE team do with the application form if the examinee does not pass the exam? (E1E12)

ANSWER: **Return the application document to the examinee**

E1F – Miscellaneous rules: external RF power amplifiers; prohibited communications; spread spectrum; auxiliary stations; Canadian amateurs operating in the U.S.; special temporary authority; control operator of an auxiliary station

As the name of this section implies, it contains a hodgepodge of questions covering sometimes obscure rules. About the only way to get these right is to memorize the answers.

The use of spread-spectrum techniques is a topic that comes up from time to time. Many amateurs feel that the rules are too restrictive. For example, spread spectrum transmissions are permitted only on amateur frequencies above 222 MHz. Other conditions apply as well. Spread spectrum emissions must not cause harmful interference to other stations employing other authorized emissions, the transmitting station must be in an area regulated by the FCC or in a country that permits SS emissions, and the transmission must not be used to obscure the meaning of any communication.

QUESTION: On what frequencies are spread spectrum transmissions permitted? (E1F01)

ANSWER: **Only on amateur frequencies above 222 MHz**

QUESTION: Which of the following conditions apply when transmitting spread spectrum emissions? (E1F09)

ANSWER: **All these choices are correct**

- A station transmitting SS emission must not cause harmful interference to other stations employing other authorized emissions.

- The transmitting station must be in an area regulated by the FCC or in a country that permits SS emissions.

- The transmission must not be used to obscure the meaning of any communication.

External RF power amplifiers

The rules governing the use of external amplifiers are also somewhat controversial. A dealer may sell an external RF power amplifier capable of operation below 144 MHz if it has not been granted FCC certification only if it was purchased in used condition from an amateur operator and is sold to another amateur operator for use at that operator's station. One of the standards that must be met by an external RF power amplifier if it is to qualify for a grant of FCC certification is that it must satisfy the FCC's spurious emission standards when operated at the lesser of 1500 watts, or its full output power.

QUESTION: Under what circumstances may a dealer sell an external RF power amplifier capable of operation below 144 MHz if it has not been granted FCC certification? (E1F03)

ANSWER: **It was purchased in used condition from an amateur operator and is sold to another amateur operator for use at that operator's station**

QUESTION: Which of the following best describes one of the standards that must be met by an external RF power amplifier if it is to qualify for a grant of FCC certification? (E1F11)

ANSWER: **It must satisfy the FCC's spurious emission standards when operated at the lesser of 1500 watts or its full output power**

Oh, Canada!

There are regulations that protects Canadian Land/Mobile operations near the US/Canadian border from interference. Amateur stations may not transmit in the 420 – 430 MHz frequency segment if they are located in the contiguous 48 states and north of Line A, which is a line roughly parallel to and south of the US-Canadian border. There is a corresponding "Line B" parallel to and north of the U.S./Canadian border.

QUESTION: Amateur stations may not transmit in which of the following frequency segments if they are located in the contiguous 48 states and north of Line A? (E1F05)

ANSWER: **420 MHz - 430 MHz**

QUESTION: Which of the following geographic descriptions approximately describes "Line A"? (E1F04)

ANSWER: **A line roughly parallel to and south of the border between the U.S. and Canada**

And, while we're on the topic of Canada, did you know that Canadian amateurs can operate in the U.S. using their Canadian license? They have the same privileges here as they do in Canada, as long as those privileges do not exceed U.S. Amateur Extra Class license privileges.

QUESTION: What privileges are authorized in the U.S. to persons holding an amateur service license granted by the government of Canada? (E1F02)

ANSWER: **The operating terms and conditions of the Canadian amateur service license, not to exceed U.S. Amateur Extra Class license privileges**

Compensated communications

As you might expect, there are questions about not making any money from operating an amateur radio station. You cannot, for example, accept any material compensation for operating an amateur radio station, except as otherwise provided in the rules. And, an amateur station may send a message to a business only when neither the amateur nor his or her employer has a pecuniary interest in the communications.

QUESTION: Which of the following types of amateur station communications are prohibited? (E1F08)

ANSWER: **Communications transmitted for hire or material compensation, except as otherwise provided in the rules**

QUESTION: When may an amateur station send a message to a business? (E1F07)

ANSWER: **When neither the amateur nor his or her employer has a pecuniary interest in the communications**

This next question is a bit of a trick question. 97.201 states that only Technician, General, Advanced or Amateur Extra Class operators may be the control operator of an auxiliary station. It's a trick question because there are also holders of Novice Class licenses, even though no new Novice licenses have been issued for many years.

QUESTION: Who may be the control operator of an auxiliary station? (E1F10)

ANSWER: **Only Technician, General, Advanced or Amateur Extra Class operators**

Special temporary authority

Some amateurs are granted special privileges called special temporary authority. The FCC issues a Special Temporary Authority (STA) to an amateur station to provide for experimental amateur communications.

QUESTION: Under what circumstances might the FCC issue a Special Temporary Authority (STA) to an amateur station? (E1F06)

ANSWER: **To provide for experimental amateur communications**

ABOUT THE AUTHOR

I have been a ham radio operator since 1971 and a radio enthusiast as long as I can remember. In addition to being an active CW operator on the HF bands:

- I blog about amateur radio at KB6NU.Com, one of the leading amateur radio blogs on the Internet.
- I am the author of the *No-Nonsense Technician Class License Study Guide* and the *No-Nonsense General Class License Study Guide*. These publications are available in PDF format, in Kindle and Nook e-book formats, and in print. See http://www.kb6nu.com/study-guides for more information.
- I am the author of *The CW Geek's Guide to Having Fun with Morse Code*, a book for those who are interested in the art of operating CW. You can find it on my website or on Amazon or Barnes&Noble. Like my other books, it's available as an e-book or in print.
- I am the author of *21 Things to Do With your Amateur Radio License*, a book for those who have been recently licensed or just getting back into the hobby. You can find it on my website, or on Amazon or Barnes&Noble. Like my other books, it's available as an e-book or in print.
- I send out a monthly column to nearly 400 amateur radio clubs in North America for publication in their newsletters.
- I teach amateur radio classes around the state of Michigan.
- I serve as the ARRL Michigan Section Training Manager and conduct amateur radio leadership workshops for amateur radio club leaders in Michigan.

You can contact me by sending e-mail to cwgeek@kb6nu.com. If you have comments or questions about any of the stuff in this book, I hope you will do so.

Also by KB6NU

No-Nonsense Technician Class License Study Guide
(for tests given between July 2014 and June 2018)

Thousands of amateur radio operators have used the No-Nonsense study guides to get into amateur radio. You can, too. You will learn everything you need to know to get your Technician Class amateur radio license. Written in a simple, easy-to-understand style, this study guide will get you on the air in no time.

No-Nonsense General Class License Study Guide
(for tests given between July 2015 and June 2019)

Written in a simple, easy-to-understand style, this study guide will help you upgrade to General Class in no time. This study guide covers every single question that you'll find on the test.

The CW Geek's Guide to Having Fun with Morse Code

The CW Geek's Guide to Having Fun with Morse Code is full of practical information that will help ham radio operators have fun learning and using Morse Code. Chapters include:

- Learning the Code. This chapter gives advice on how to learn the code, including recommendations for programs and websites that you can use for free.
- Getting on the Air. This chapter describes, in my "no nonsense" style how to tune in CW signals, how to make contact, and then what to do once you have made contact.
- Choosing a Key. This chapter describes the different types of keys available and how to choose the one that's right for you.
- Keyers. This chapter describes the different types of keyers and how to connect them to your radio.
- References and Resources. This section includes information on Q-signals, RST signal reporting, abbreviations, CW clubs, and other resources that will be useful for amateur radio operators.

21 Things to Do After You Get Your Amateur Radio License

Congratulations! You passed the test and have an amateur radio license. Now what? *21 Things to Do After You Get Your Amateur Radio License* tells you what. The 21 different activities in the book will not only suggest things you can do with your ham license, but more importantly, how to have fun

with amateur radio. You'll discover:
- How and why to join a club
- What things to think about before you buy a radio
- How to set up a "shack"
- Why you should build a kit or an antenna
- How to learn Morse Code
- How to participate in public-service and emergency communications events
- Plus much, much, more...

You can purchase e-book versions of all these titles on KB6NU.Com. Print versions are available from Amazon.

Made in the USA
Middletown, DE
09 June 2023

31882559R00139